Tinderbox

MEGAN DUNN

GALLEY BEGGAR PRESS

First published in 2017
by Galley Beggar Press Limited
37 Dover Street, Norwich NR2 3LG

Excerpts from *Fahrenheit 451 SparkNotes Literature Guide*
have been used with permission from Spark Publishing,
a division of Barnes and Noble.

Paperback ISBN: 978-1-910296-82-0
Limited edition ISBN: 978-1-910296-84-4

Text and design by Tetragon, London
Printed and bound in Great Britain by Clays Ltd, St Ives plc

For the book people,
especially disenfranchised booksellers.

Foreword

Ray Bradbury's *Fahrenheit 451* is one of those classic novels you study in high school. Later on in life, if you're a chain bookseller, you might find yourself shelving it or merchandising a copy next to *Black Beauty* in a banned books display. Or plucking the hazardous *Fahrenheit 451* Cliff Notes from the in-store spinner and selling it to some poor kid's mother.

Fahrenheit 451 depicts a futuristic society in which books are banned and firemen, instead of putting out fires, confiscate books and ignite them. Fahrenheit 451 is the temperature at which book paper catches fire. At the disposal of the firemen is a mechanical hound and inside the hound's muzzle is a needle programmed to paralyse its prey.

Bradbury's *Fahrenheit 451* is a cautionary tale about the perils of anti-intellectualism and the high price of freedom. If you're not careful it's the kind of book that chases you into adulthood, still burning.

I don't remember ever selling a copy to anyone but myself.

The Cutting Room

'IT WAS A PLEASURE TO BURN.' In the spring of 1950 Ray Bradbury sat in the basement of the Lawrence Powell library at UCLA, took a dime out of his pocket and slotted it into the small timer. Clunk. He struck the keys of the typewriter; each letter of the alphabet sprang forward printed, its likeness on paper, then snapped back into place. Students sat at the other eleven pay-by-the-hour typewriters in the basement of the library and pounded the keys. Bradbury added his own fingertips to the stampede. He was following a character along the white sheet of the page. Guy Montag left the fire station after a day of burning books and took the tube to the suburbs. Montag emerged on a blank street and turned a corner. The wind picked up. Autumn leaves scattered. The sentence came to a full stop.

Bradbury stretched in his chair and rubbed his forehead; his eyes felt heavy. His back ached and his right leg had gone to sleep. His wife and baby daughter were waiting at home. Outside, the sun was setting over L.A. but he couldn't see it. The basement had no windows. Bradbury glanced at the student sitting in front of him. Her blonde ponytail had flared on the edge of his vision all day. She typed in a neat, even rhythm as though she knew exactly where she was going and what she wanted to

3

say. The blonde unwound the last page from her typewriter and gathered together a thick ream of paper. Bradbury watched as she stood up and walked out of the basement of the library. Her pony tail swayed from side to side. She didn't look back.

Bradbury had to keep going. He wrote in half hour instalments. His fingers raced over the keys. The typewriter outran his thoughts. The story barely paused for Bradbury to stop and add another dime. He finished the first draft of *Fahrenheit 451* in nine days: a 25,000 word story called *The Fireman*. It cost him $9.80.

The timer went off.

In December 2009 I stood behind the till at Borders Kingston-Upon-Thames and held the scanner over the binc sticker on the back of a book. The scanner flashed red as it registered the title, beeped and added the price to the total. A fleet of Borders stores had opened throughout the UK. Born in the USA, the typical Borders' two-storey stores were large, friendly super-markets where browsers could freely roam the aisles. Borders' presence on the local high street had once seemed as assured as a Starbucks Grande Cappuccino. Now size and range had become its downfall. 'Is the discount on there?' The customer glanced at the total on the cash register. During the sale I noticed customers had developed a heightened distrust of technology. 'Yes,' I said. 'The books are all half price.' I pressed Enter on the till. The receipt began to print. I handed the customer the Eftpos machine. 'You can swipe your card now.' He swiped. We waited for the transaction to complete. 'Does this mean you're all out of jobs?' he asked. 'No,' I said. 'Borders is in voluntary administration.' I explained the difference between voluntary administration and liquidation. It was a difference that sounded tenuous even to me. The customer checked his itemised receipt as I stuffed the last book in his bag, noticing with distaste that it was a Dan Brown novel. Satisfied, the customer looked up. 'Thank you.' He grabbed his bag of books. 'Good luck,' he said. I didn't bother to reply. I didn't charge him 5p for the plastic bag either. I was sick of putting out fires.

At Borders all the staff wore lanyards that said 'Happy to help.' I was not happy to help. I worked at Borders because I wanted to be a writer. I stood behind the till dressed in a red Borders sweatshirt and a pair of jeans. My fingertips were sore from entering reduced prices into the tills. My wrists ached from bagging. My shoulders were tense. I watched customers strip books from the shelves. Pages curled at their corners and crumpled. My face felt scorched. My smile had long since melted away. A conga line of crazed shoppers wound around the ground floor. I turned towards the front of the queue. 'Next.'

I picked up the scanner. Beep. Beep. I had been with Borders UK for seven years by the time it was placed into voluntary administration. I was originally hired as a part-time Christmas temp at Borders Islington in 2002, but the job had stuck. I transferred to Borders Norwich in 2005 and was part of the team that opened Borders Dundee in 2006. I'd started thinking about *Fahrenheit 451* during those last critical months when I was the sales manager at Borders Kingston-Upon Thames. In the wake of Amazon's Kindle it seemed unlikely that books would ever be banned: instead books are commodified, turned into movies and TV series, rated and recommended in Goodreads, their individual sales histories quantified on Nielsen Bookdata and in the fathomless depths of the Amazon Sales Ranking system. Even the Kindle was named by a branding consultant who suggested the word to Amazon because it means to light a fire. The branding consultant thought that 'kindle' was an apt metaphor for reading and intellectual excitement.

I bet Ray Bradbury would have agreed. The book people at the end of *Fahrenheit 451* wouldn't need to memorise volumes of literature anymore. Now they could store their libraries on their Kindles or iPads. Project Gutenberg has been in the business of archiving classics since 1971. There are currently over 42,000 e-books available in the free domain. *Fahrenheit 451* is not of them. Not because it has been banned. Quite the contrary. Ray Bradbury's sci-fi classic has not been out of print since it was first published by Ballantine Books in 1953. The novel is still protected by copyright. If I'd thought about that more at the time I started writing it might have scared me.

I remembered the mechanical hound from *Fahrenheit 451*, the watchdog of the firemen, who hunted down the literate like prey. I wondered if the mechanical hound was as shonky as the Elonex e-reader we'd been selling at Borders for the past couple of months. Our slow-witted display device was fixed to the main information desk on a long plastic lead. All I needed to memorise was its unique selling points. It had five adjustable font sizes and a built-in dictionary. The Elonex e-reader also came pre-loaded with one hundred classics. As a selling point this was not unique. The books cost nothing because the authors were dead and the works had fallen out of copyright.

'Does it have a reading light?' Customers came pre-loaded with their own set of great expectations that the Elonex e-reader could not always fufill.

The future arrived and it was not science fiction. On Christmas Eve Borders UK was liquidated, forty-five stores were closed and over one thousand employees were made redundant.

It was not a pleasure to burn. In the spring of 2013, I sat at the desk in the spare room of my rented apartment in Wellington. I'd just joined National Novel Writing Month: an online community for anyone who has ever wanted to write a novel. On November 1st participants begin working towards the goal of writing a 50,000 word novel by 11:59pm on November 30th. Entry is free. I signed up and chose my online alias. I'd decided to write a homage to *Fahrenheit 451* but I didn't enter a synposis of my novel on the site. What if it sounded a bit... weird? 50,000 divided by 30 = 1,666.66667 words per day. How hard could it be?

The NaNoWriMo site has a word count graph. I could track my indvidual progress against the pack. I had thirty days and one major weakness. Structure. That was okay. I could borrow Ray's.

I picked up the copy of *Fahrenheit 451* on my desk. An illustration of flames licked the right-hand corner of the cover. I hadn't read *Fahrenheit 451* since I was in high school, but I remembered the gist: in the future firemen burn books. Wars are fought in forty-five minutes. People are written into TV programmes broadcast through walls as big as screens. Besides, there was no time for stalling. I had less than forty-five minutes before work. I set the timer on my iPhone and typed the first sentence of *Fahrenheit 451* into Word. Sunlight warmed my face through the window. I squinted at the white glare on the screen. I couldn't see. It was time for a coffee.

In the kitchen I flicked on the kettle and scooped three spoonfuls into the plunger. *Fahrenheit 451* is divided into 'The Hearth and the Salamander', 'The Sieve and the Sand' and 'Burning Bright'. The kettle boiled. I plunged.

I returned to my desk and took a sip of coffee. I wasn't a fireman like Bradbury's character, Guy Montag. I'd never burned a book, but I'd been burned by them. I hadn't been able to sell my first semi-autobiographical novel. And my career as a bookseller had also been extinguished. All I needed to do was start at the beginning. I took another sip of coffee.

The timer went off.

The next morning I sat down at my desk with a fresh cup of coffee and new resolve. Day 2. 3,333.33333 words to go. I needed to catch up on the word count from yesterday. I'd decided to tackle my homage from the perspective of Clarisse McClellan. I typed *Fahrenheit 451* into Google and found a website called SparkNotes that contained abbreviated analysis of classic novels for students and other time-poor readers. Brilliant. SparkNotes had been organised into three main sections: general info; summary and analysis; and study tools. I scrolled through the character summaries to refresh my memory. SparkNotes described Clarisse as a beautiful teenager who introduced Montag to the world's potential for beauty and meaning with her 'gentle innocence and curiosity'. I tried to imagine what Clarisse was thinking. Did she drink coffee? I didn't drink coffee when I was 17. I pictured Clarisse in her bedroom with a pencil and a piece of paper. The words were coming hot and fast from her own mind, she was writing without thinking, she was living the life I wanted to live.

It was a pleasure to write, I typed. 3,333.33333 − 6 words = 3,327.33333.

I was starting with a lie.

Maybe Clarisse liked to write quickly, not stopping to think too hard. If she wrote fast enough her words were completely fresh, as though they had not come from her own mind. It was mad how writing could be like that. A rush of sentences down the highway of the page, paragraphs careening around corners.

Mad, it seemed like such a Bradbury word, exuberant and full of zeal!

I stopped writing and look at the timer on my iPhone. Three minutes. I took another sip of coffee and stared at the words on the screen. Maybe in the future it was also illegal to write. Finally I'd had an idea with some traction. If Clarisse wasn't allowed to read books, then she shouldn't be permitted to write them either.

I reset the timer and typed: *She glanced at the curtains drawn across her bedroom window as though she was being watched. The fabric shimmered, struck with sunlight from the other side of the glass. Her right hand ached from holding the pencil. She soothed her writing wrist, cupping her fingers around it, like a bracelet.*

I felt Clarisse's pain. No one writes by hand anymore. It hurts.

From the city the distant roar of cars, speeding beyond billboards. I flicked back to Google, opened a new search, deleted the word roar.

Someone knocked on my door.

I was 14 when I first read *Fahrenheit 451*. I wore a blue tartan uniform and sat at my wooden school desk at Western Heights High School in Rotorua. The mechanical hound bounded through the desecrated city. The hound ran on eight legs like a spider as helicopters flew overhead, blades spinning. The hound was at the service of the firemen. Wars were fought in 45 minutes. The parlour walls were lit by giant TV screens. In *Fahrenheit 451* Montag's wife Mildred starred in a soap opera filmed live from her living room. She called the people on TV her family. Mildred and Montag slept in single beds like my grandparents. At night, she wore a pair of 'seashells' in her ears that helped her sleep.

Mildred. It's such an antiquated name. I don't know anyone called Mildred. The word 'parlour' still seems quaint to me and Fahrenheit is not a contemporary currency. In the sixties and seventies the Celsius scale replaced Fahrenheit in almost all countries except America. I suspect this is why Bradbury's novel has never entered the mainstream vernacular in the same way as Orwell's 1984. I've watched Big Brother. He doesn't watch me. Like Orwell's telescreens the parlour walls in *Fahrenheit 451* also predate Reality TV.

Mildred's favourite TV programme is called *The White Clown*.

'What do you think the white clown means?' our English teacher asked us in fourth form.

'That TV is stupid, eh, Miss?' a boy said.

Everyone laughed.

'And why do you think that?' she asked.

'Because clowns are funny.'

'But clowns can be scary too, can't they?'

She was right. I had recently read Stephen King's IT. On the cover was an image of a clown in a red fright wig. IT was much more frightening than *Fahrenheit 451*. I couldn't get to sleep after reading IT; I worried that the clown in the red fright wig was hiding underneath my single bed.

The bell rang and a chorus of chairs scraped backwards. I shut the lid of my desk for the day. I enjoyed studying *Fahrenheit 451* in class but I wasn't afraid the mechanical hound was going to chase me into the future. I walked home from school. Jet streams flared across the sky. My drink bottle sloshed up and down in my bag. Sweat trickled down my back. I stopped at the rusted red train tracks half way along the road. I looked both ways; only the heat rising in the distance. There weren't any book people walking along the tracks and there weren't any trains either. At home I lay on the couch in my school uniform, legs slung over the coffee table.

'What's a hearth?' I asked Mum.

'The hearth is the area at the front of an old fireplace,' Mum said. 'People used to sit around the hearth in the evenings back before there was TV.'

Mum had just got home too and was dressed in her nurse's smock and red cardigan. The ironing-board creaked to life as Mum set it up in the lounge in front of the TV. The fireplace in our rented flat was covered with a piece of white gib-board. Mum poured water from a little plastic jug into the iron. The iron emitted a hiss and a faint burst of steam.

'Shit,' Mum said. Something bad had happened on the news again.

In 1989 my dystopia was nuclear, a mushroom cloud, the day after tomorrow. In 1990 I watched the Gulf War in night vision. Missiles sparked across the screen. Mint green.

Arachnid, the mechanical hound tracked his prey at night. He ran on eight legs. His proboscis dispensed a lethal injection of procaine.

The timer went off.

It was not a pleasure to write. Day 3. I woke up at 6.30, opened my MacBook Air and logged in to NaNoWriMo. Some participants had already clocked up 10,000+ words. What kind of novels were they writing? Didn't they eat? Have lives? Standards? I set the timer on my iPhone for thirty minutes. Each sentence felt like a squeeze. *The rain began to download on the domed roof of the school,* twelve words. *The rain was always programmed to fall at this time,* ten words. Why was I having trouble getting into character? I was once a teenage girl, admittedly not a beautiful blonde one. I cast my mind back. What mattered in high school?

Enter Montag, slightly unshaven, a fireman in a black and orange suit. On his chest the company insignia: a phoenix rising.

I bet Clarisse had a crush on Montag. Crush. A short rush mounted by that high C.

The rain fell systematically on the domed roof of the school, like data collating, reacting, endlessly responding.

'This used to be my high school. But it's changed. When I was here the building was wooden. Of course we would never use the world's natural resources so carelessly now. When I was your age I didn't know what I wanted to be. So if some of you feel the same way, I sympathise.'

Seventy-two words. A school visit. Yes! What could be more fitting. In our last year of high school we were always being pestered with work experience opportunities. Wasn't it entirely possible that Montag might have been sent to Clarisse's high school to lecture the students on the joys of becoming a fireman? And wasn't it even more possible that she thought he was hot? I imagined what kind of lecture Montag might give if he was recruiting teenagers for the fire department.

'Paper burns at Fahrenheit 451,' he told the class. 'Flames curdle and blacken the pages till each book crumbles to ash. A library takes time to burn. The other firemen and I stand back and watch it together. We always know that we've done the right thing. We harvest the ash and use it as compost. In the fire brigade we value the future of this planet. Our creed is: we burn, so that you don't have to.'

Another seventy-eight words. My updated creed was a nice flourish. Bradbury was prescient but not quite so prescient as to predict global warming, recycling and the imminent extinction of the bumble bee.

A fireman sympathising, I decided Clarisse wanted to write this down, to capture it in her diary. *Even his name sounded exotic, like a character in a story that she might write and she didn't know how it would end.*

I looked at the timer. One minute left: *The fireman took his helmet off and held it on his knee. The teenager watched. Her legs crossed and uncrossed. She wondered what it might feel like to run her hands over the 451 emblazoned on his helmet, to feel the fireman's number embossed beneath her touch.*

She glanced at the wedding ring that cordoned him off. His voice was even, almost plain. She sensed that he was not a man who often had an audience. Perhaps he was someone who slipped through life unnoticed, despite his status, his uniform, his touch. Did his wife know he was sad? Did she even know him at all? Every time his eyes flickered over her face, she could feel the heat rising, as though she was burning and he held the match.

305 words. Phew.

The timer went off.

I was beginning to think Clarisse was a little naïve. After work in the evening I needed to write another 1072 words to make my daily count. Instead, I lay on the couch drinking red wine and trying to read *Fahrenheit 451*, while my boyfriend played *Grand Theft Auto* on the PlayStation. His car swerved round corners as I turned pages.

Clarisse first meets Montag one evening when they are both out walking. Walking is unusual in *Fahrenheit 451*. Let's not forget Bradbury wrote the first draft in the basement of the Los Angeles library. I've never been to LA but I'm told everyone drives there. *Fahrenheit 451* was inspired by an earlier short story of Bradbury's called 'The Pedestrian'. The story was about a writer who lives in a television-centred society. The writer is arrested by the police one night when he is out walking and taken to the Psychiatric Centre for Research on Regressive Tendencies. Bradbury never learnt to drive. I've never learnt to drive either.

My boyfriend sped around the city in *Grand Theft Auto* with the car radio on. Eighties pop songs drifted in and out of my consciousness. I took another sip of wine, turned the page. The fireman's truck in *Fahrenheit 451* is called a salamander. Montag the fireman and his big black hose. A teenage girl can find a phallus in just about anything. So can a middle-aged woman. Bradbury described Clarisse's face as milk crystal. What the heck was milk crystal? In the book he said Clarisse's dress was white and it whispered. I bet it did. I know the relationship between Clarisse and Montag isn't meant to be sexual, but she's a teenager and he's a married man.

And she also twirls a dandelion under his chin and asks him if he's happy. Then she tells him to taste the rain. I snorted. It was pretty forward stuff for the 1950s. I wouldn't twirl a dandelion under a fireman's chin now. Let alone ask a married man to open his mouth and let the rain in.

I flicked back to Bradbury's introduction for more explanation.

He was living in an apartment in Venice, California with his wife and baby daughter when he wrote the first draft of F451. He needed more quiet to do his work. He had no money to rent an office but one day when he was at UCLA he'd overheard typing from the basement and went down to see what the story was.

Bradbury sounded like a nice enough guy. I placed the book on the arm of the sofa and cruised Wikipedia. He was married for 56 years to Marguerite McClure. She was the only woman he ever dated. They had four daughters. What did his wife and daughters think of Clarrise? Bradbury also wrote a semi-autobiographical novel called *Dandelion Wine*. I've drunk a lot of wine, but never dandelion. In 1971, the Apollo 15 astronauts named a crater on the moon the 'Dandelion Crater' in honour of the book. I imagined an astronaut reading *Dandelion Wine* at zero gravity, turning the pages suspended in mid-air.

'Hey baby, what'll it be?' My boyfriend picked up a prostitute on *Grand Theft Auto*. The prostitute gave my boyfriend's alter ego a blowjob in the front seat of the car. Afterwards she got out, slammed the door and said: 'You wore my pussy out. You men are all the same. You think you want one thing but really you want everything.'

I picked up my glass of wine. It was empty.

The timer went off.

The next morning I was still in bed at 7am. My mouth tasted fusty from the red wine. Day 4 and I'd already run out of time. I'd have to make the word count up later. 'Are you getting out of bed?' my boyfriend asked. 'In a minute.' I searched the Aro Valley Video website. I was lucky the shop was still in business. The future hasn't been kind to music or DVDs. Now everyone streams music and movies online. I hadn't bought a CD since I worked at Borders but I still rented DVD's. Not because I cared about the customer experience, but because I was too much of a luddite to work out how to download illegally. Aro Valley had the best back catalogue in Wellington. Not just the mainstream fodder but the good shit. I could pick *Fahrenheit 451* up after work. Watching the film might spark something.

Watching the film did spark something. Memories. I'd seen it before. I was turning into my mother who could never remember the films she'd already watched either. I'd probably first watched François Truffaut's 1966 version of *Fahrenheit 451* when I was in my twenties and at art school. Truffaut was French and even though the film had dated it was arty.

The film was shot in England at Pinewood studios. Which was probably why I originally thought Ray Bradbury was a British author. Truffaut had cast the actress Julie Christie as both Mildred and Clarisse. Christie was British. Bradbury was not happy about this decision because Clarisse was meant to be a schoolgirl. Not a blonde bombshell from the swinging sixties who was in her mid-twenties. The age change didn't bother me. I liked Julie Christie. She looked especially hot as Montag's wife, wearing a long silken wig with bangs.

I wasn't happy that Truffaut had removed the character of the mechanical hound from the film. Bradbury thought the hound was an essential element of the story because it showed what the future looked like. I agreed. However, I understood that it would have been technically challenging for Truffaut to create a convincing mechanical hound for the screen in 1966. Especially if the hound had to be menacing. There was no CGI in those days.

I was non-plussed by Truffaut's *Fahrenheit 451*. I didn't like Montag, who was played by the Austrian actor Oskar Werner. Truffaut wrote in his diary that *Fahrenheit 451* was his 'saddest and most difficult' filmmaking experience. Apparently, he didn't like Oskar Werner either.

Instead of getting sucked into the film's plot, I got sidetracked watching the DVD extras. In the production shots Julie Christie and Francois Truffaut sat on a curb in the suburbs. Truffaut held a bottle of champagne and poured them both a glass. In the background was the house that doubled as Montag's home in the film. The stark white limbs of trees framed the scene like kindling. Even the production shots seemed fused with sadness, with the film's eventual critical and commercial failure. Truffaut's head bent towards Christie. What were they talking about?

'I think that he was out of his element linguistically and geographically,' said Columbia Professor Annette Insdorf in *The Making of Fahrenheit 451*. Her lipstick was full bodied like a good merlot. She looked like a woman who knows.

Fahrenheit 451 was the first film Truffaut had made in colour. It was also the first – and only – film he made in English. Truffaut only spoke French; luckily for him Julie Christie spoke French too. Whereas my own French was limited to what I learnt in high school: Ca va? Ca va bien.

Insdorf pronounced the film Truffaut's passionate homage to literature, to the written word. Ditto. My homage to *Fahrenheit 451* was going to be a searing feminist rewrite of Bradbury's classic, like Jean Rhys's *Wide Sargasso Sea*, only blonder.

I watched *The Making of Fahrenheit 451* hoping I'll relate to Christie's point of view. Instead it was the film's editor I really took to. Thom Noble.

I empathised with Thom's plight. The cutting room was next door to the fire station on set. Thom could look out the window and watch the fire engine sail past. *Fahrenheit 451* was the first film he had edited. In the documentary he wore a Joan Miro T-shirt. He seemed chipper and unpretentious.

'By the end of the film Francois was able to say to me, "have a good weekend," but that was about the extent of his English,' Thom laughed, on the DVD extras.

'You're off topic,' my inner critic said, as I sat in front of the TV with the laptop on my lap and scrolled Wikipedia for more facts.

Time magazine had called the film a 'weirdly gay little picture that assails with both horror and humor all forms of tyranny over the mind of man. It strongly supports the widely held suspicion that Julie Christie cannot actually act. Though she plays two women of diametrically divergent dispositions, they seem in her portrayal to differ only in their hairdos'.

Watching the film did spark something. An idea. Maybe I could rewrite *Fahrenheit 451* alternating between the characters of Clarisse and Mildred. Like Julie Christie I could change my hairdo.

The timer went off.

Day 5 and I'm already running a 4,686 word deficit. In the morning I reopened SparkNotes for a quick precis of Mildred's character. SparkNotes suggested that Mildred's obsession with TV was a means to avoid confronting her life. It didn't seem to occur to SparkNotes that watching TV was her life.

Mildred lay in bed listening to her seashells on shuffle. The rain slashed against the skylight and dribbled down the glass in long rivulets. Her head was fuzzy and her mouth tasted of red wine. She reached for her iPhone on the bedside table and knocked over a wine glass. The glass rolled on its side and pointed at her like a compass. The last drop of Merlot rolled towards the rim. She picked up her iPhone and swiped her finger across the screen. 2:49pm. Soon the neighbourhood children would be coming home from school. She turned her seashells off. The rain was always sharpest before it stopped.

107 words. Not bad. I stared at my own reflection in my laptop screen and fluffed up my hair so it was a little more bouffy. Mildred opened the bedside drawer, threw the seashells inside, took out a container of pills, unscrewed the lid and popped a couple more. She walked over to the window and gazed at the white flaky tree trunks that lined the suburb.

I noticed that the view from Mildred's window looked uncannily like the suburb in Truffaut's film. Where was the film shot? That dreary cul-de-sac with its stifled sense of pathos – and what were the trees outside the window actually called?

Mildred shook her head and swallowed. 154 words. Her favourite programme The White Clown would be on soon and she needed to get ready. She stood up and smiled at her reflection in the mirrored door of the wardrobe. Her mouth was crimson and cracked. Another 191 words. And she looked like Julie Christie. She was wearing the flouncy apricot pyjamas from the film. It was a very frou frou costume, one I'd recognise anywhere. It also matched the hue of their bed linen on set. The retro décor in the film added a certain je nas sais quoi. Truffaut said he shot the film exactly as though it was in black and white, which either meant the auteur was lying or he was colourblind. The whole film screamed colour. The red fire engine! The red postbox! The orange bathroom!

Julie Christie in those apricot pyjamas – what a peach! In the film Truffaut had renamed the wife's character Linda. Maybe Linda sounded sexier in French?

Linda reached under her husband's pillow. The book was still there. She traced her index finger along its spine. She looked around the bedroom as though Francois Truffaut was standing in the shadows on set watching her every move. ('Tres bein,' he whispered, '39 mots.') Then she slid the book out from underneath the pillow, brushed her hand over its cover, dust collected on her palm and also a bit on her apricot pyjamas. The book had a different energy to an iPhone or tablet. She could feel the life force in the paper.

She flicked it open and the pages sent a rush of old air over her face. She read the title, 'Are you there God? It's me, Margaret.'

The author's name was not Margaret. Are you there God? It's me, Margaret was first published in 1970. I thought of the author – Judy Blume – writing the book about Margaret that Linda was now reading in my redraft. It was a great feminist touch, even if I did say so myself. Truffaut hadn't focused on women's literature in his film. Touche. That was something I was going to amend in my rewrite. I wondered what Judy Blume's total word count was.

One sentence added to another. I paused. The house hummed around me, like silence, but more than silence. Also my laptop was whirring. I slipped my hand underneath it. Hot. It helped to visualise Bradbury's Mildred as Truffaut's Linda. I just had to mentally insert Julie Christie into new scenes of my own imagining.

In my rewrite the rain had stopped. Sunlight angled against the windows trying to find a way in. Linda walked into the en-suite, stepped out of her pyjamas (I couldn't help but think of the delicate handwash they'd require later) and turned the shower on. Warm water pooled in her right ear as thought it was a seashell. Her husband would want to talk to her when he got home. He'd want to explain why he was breaking the law by hiding books in their house. But she was sick of talking. A siren flared in the suburbs.

'Are you there God? C'est moi, Linda.' She wrapped her wet hair in a towel and moved back to the window. She pressed her hand against the triple-glazed glass and felt the dying heat of the sun. Two silhouettes stretched across the street. The school-girl from next door slunk along beside the fireman like a white weasel. The girl practically turned cartwheels around him. Her husband looked attractive in his black shiny uniform. She stood in the window and watched.

The timer went off.

Day 6 and my redraft had been hijacked by Julie Christie's apricot pyjamas. The film kept unspooling onto the page. I couldn't make it stop. The characters in the book and the actors in the film had blended in my mind. I had no idea how Mildred felt. Not the character Bradbury had first created in 1950. Perhaps it would have helped if he'd specified what she wore? I couldn't fully imagine his vision of the future in Fahrenheit 451 either. It didn't pop in Technicolor. For Bradbury's Mildred finding a book in the house probably felt as strange and repellent as finding a severed human hand in a rubbish bin, and this made me aware – with a kind of horror – that books were my life. Books were the only assets I owned in our rented flat. They were spread out on the table like tarot cards and lined up on my chest of drawers, waiting to be read or at least alphabetised. A faded copy of The Idiot had buckled in the sun on my windowsill. I still hadn't read Dostoevsky. The weight of the past pressed down on me. Or maybe it was just Dostoevsky's oppressive word count? I closed my laptop and walked away from my desk. Who was I to take on Bradbury's masterpiece?

'Maybe you're not a writer,' my inner critic said.

I walked past the bedroom and my boyfriend stirred and rolled over.

He looked at me. 'I thought you were writing this morning.'

'I am writing,' I said.

In the kitchen, light twisted through the window, casting doubt over everything. I got up an hour early so I could write for longer. 'What are you waiting for?' my inner critic said. 'Some of the other NaNoWriMo participants are halfway.' I flicked the jug on and took the milk out of the fridge. While I waited for the jug to boil I made breakfast. Two weetabix, two sugars: four words. Outside, it was raining. That's why the rain had crept into the writing. 'Your work is too autobiographical,' my inner critic said. I took a bite of weetabix. At least that lived up to expectations. After breakfast and coffee I felt intellectually frisked, ready for another instalment on the timer.

I returned to my desk and sat down. My back ached. My eyes were tired. But there was a book inside me and it wanted to get out. The book whispered, 'Forget about the word count.

Just write what comes. Don't censor it. It doesn't matter if it's autobiographical.'

At least that's what I think it was whispering.

In 2001, I stamped a reduced-price sticker on a book and stared out of the shop window at Stoke Newington High Street. I was 28-years-old and worked part-time in a bargain bookshop. Dust billowed before my eyes, swirling and falling onto the Wordsworth Classics display in the window. The display was covered in a fine layer of soot from the red double-decker buses that swept along the high street carrying the cargo of London on their worn backs.

Since moving to London, I had already been fired from several jobs: I was an office temp who couldn't type. I was a sandwich maker who abhorred tuna. And I was a bartender at a pub called *The Purple Turtle* the day the twin towers were bombed. On 9/11 I woke up next to a fellow employee who had given me a tab of ecstasy the night before. We sat on the couch and watched the twin towers burning. Smoke filled the sky. 'I can't believe it,' he said.

I couldn't believe it either.

I had only been living in London for nine months but it felt like forever. The bargain bookstore was located next to a bank and a Wetherspoon's. I worked alone. The books arrived every few days in boxes. I opened each delivery. My hopes for intellectual stimulation were often flattened by a shipment of thin scholastic workbooks. I wedged Dickens and Dostoevsky into alphabetical order. A row of spines needled each other for space on the Wordsworth Classics shelf. I was often challenged by *The Idiot*. It was a very fat book and took up a lot of room.

Lined up in their blue jackets the Wordsworth Classics held the pungent aroma of the past. In between deliveries, I re-read the Hans Christian Andersen fairy tales I had loved as a child. I related to the poverty of 'The Little Match Girl' and I was still scared of the three dogs in 'The Tinderbox'.

'This must be a wonderful job,' an old lady said. 'I'd love to work in a bookshop.'

I sat behind the till picking at my split ends.

A foreigner in a shiny suit stumbled into the store, holding a briefcase. He looked like a refugee. Perhaps a Doctor or a Professor of Linguistics?

He opened the briefcase and took out a mechanical turtle.

'Ten pounds?' he enquired.

I shook my head.

He flipped the turtle over and showed me the hatch for the double AA batteries.

'Ten pounds?'

'No.'

He stood for a moment just holding the turtle by his heart.

'Ten pounds?'

Now that I worked at the bargain bookshop I felt tainted by the remainders. I too was one of life's remainders. I couldn't afford a mechanical turtle even if I wanted one. I felt as grim as the pigeons that roosted in the sign above the shop door. In the evening the sky wriggled out of its grey sweatshirt and pulled down its black tattered sleeves. I got up and flicked the lights off. I sometimes caught a silhouette of myself in the glass pane of the door as I locked up. My face a wan shadow like the little match girl. The pigeons cooed. A beggar sat next to his black dog outside the bank. The beggar was also covered in dust. And his dog wasn't summoned from the power of the Tinderbox to bring him riches. Instead the beggar's empty hand was outstretched like the mouth of the cash register I left open in the evenings.

'London's a big place for a little Kiwi,' Mickey said. 'Things will get better. Everyone has to pay their dues.'

At the time I believed him. Mickey and I were in love. He was an artist, but he worked at Borders Charing Cross Road. The staff had nicknamed him Mickey Romance because he worked in the romance section. In 2002 my working holiday visa was running out so we decided to get married. Our wedding was held in the Gold Suite at Hackney Town Hall. I wore an electric blue kimono. Mickey wore a blue tie. My mother cried.

The timer went off.

SPARKNOTES SUGGESTED ESSAY TOPIC:

Discuss Montag's relationship with Mildred. Is this a typical marital relationship in their culture?
    Yes.

I woke up at 6.30am and opened my MacBook Air. I'd been writing for nine days. Total word count: 6,762. By this time in 1950 Bradbury was reaching for the last dime in his bag of change. He spent $9.80 and produced a masterpiece. Why couldn't I be a genius? The failure of my first novel hounded me. It wasn't even worth $9.80. I couldn't think of a plot. And I still wrote in disjointed fragments. My own life kept interrupting and changing the script. I wanted to get away from autobiography. I wanted to create with a capital C.

Whenever Bradbury needed a break from his draft of *Fahrenheit 451* he left the basement and ran upstairs to the UCLA library to browse the shelves for inspiration. He chose books at random and opened the pages to find interesting quotations. For Bradbury being in the library was a wonderful experience. He dashed up and down the stairs opening one book after another, plucking sentences straight from the page.

He was a wise man. He was also prolific.

I spent the rest of the day cruising BrainyQuotes instead of trying to to put the pieces of my plot together. My book was a total mess. A mish-mash of free floating memories.

Q. I wonder if writing was this difficult for Bradbury?

A. It wasn't.

I found a website called GlamAmor dedicated to the history of fashion in film. The chick that ran GlamAmor valued the cinematic potential of Julie Christie's hair in a way that *Time*

Magazine never would. She wrote, 'Julie's hair is beyond beautiful and has always been one of my favourite points of inspiration over the years.'

The webpage was helpfully illustrated with numerous photographs of Christie.

Her up-do was particularly prominent in *Doctor Zhivago*. Check.

Then there was the famous asymmetrical bob from *Shampoo*. Check.

I noticed in the string of enthusiastic comments that there seemed to be no end to the influence of Julie Christie's hair.

As the author of GlamAmor said, 'That 1960s bedhead hair of hers – along with Brigitte Bardot's – never seems to go out of style and has continued to be a popular request in today's hair salons.'

I updated my profile picture in Facebook to a photograph of Julie Christie.

'Have you had a haircut?' asked an old male manager from Borders.

'I'm glad you noticed,' I said.

Truffaut's film was also filled with quotations. According to Annette Insdorf *Fahrenheit 451* was made during his 'Hitchcockian period.'

In one scene Julie Christie adjusted a self-portrait on the wall and a Penguin Classic fell from behind the frame. She flicked it away with her hand. 'Eww.'

Apparently this was a reference to a scene in Hitchcock's *The Birds*, when a bird darts out from behind a picture frame and attacks Tippi Hendren.

The Birds was much scarier than *Fahrenheit 451*. The pen might be mightier than the sword, but it was rarely frightening. Unless you were holding it, of course.

The white screen wavered in front of me.

Also Microsoft Word kept crashing. Word was not a great programme to use on a MacBook. Maybe it just wasn't a great programme full stop.

'Why have you got so many windows open?' my boyfriend asked.

'I don't know.'

'Just force quit,' my boyfriend said.

The timer went off.

Christmas 2002: I dropped off my CV at the main information desk of Borders Islington. I got a call a week later. My interview went more or less according to plan. I sat in the manager's office in my best pair of jeans trying to look earnest and helpful. I explained that I loved reading and writing. I said I was doing a writing class at City Lit on Tuesdays but I was available to work every other day, including weekends and evenings.

'And if a middle aged lady came in and asked for a great summer read, what would you recommend?' the interviewer asked.

'I'd probably ask her what kind of books she enjoyed.'

'A good story, escapism, something that keeps you turning the page.'

'I might ask if she had tried *The No. 1 Ladies Detective Agency*.'

The interviewer nodded. 'And what about a boy looking for a Father's Day gift?'

'Bill Bryson.'

My time in the bargain bookstore had served me well.

'Great.' The interviewer turned the piece of paper over. 'Can you describe what makes really good customer service?'

'Well, someone who is attentive, but not too attentive. Customers need to be able to browse. It's important to be able to flick through the books and just relax. That's why the philosophy of Borders is so great and there's the Starbucks upstairs.'

The interviewer smiled. 'Can you think of any other ways that Borders is different from the competition on the high street?'

I shifted in my seat.

'How would you describe the décor at Borders?' the interviewer asked.

I thought about the high black book shelves at Waterstones. I preferred the traditional library atmosphere that Waterstones was renowned for. Borders stores were messier. Books were left everywhere like bric-a-brac. And Borders played music over the store speakers. The walls were...

'Terracotta?' I said.

'And do you have any questions you'd like to ask me?' the interviewer smiled.

'Is there a staff discount?'

The timer went off.

In London I started to write because it was cheap. Writing cost me nothing other than time. I inherited an old clunky laptop. The laptop became my tinderbox. I struck words from the keys. Writing kindled early memories.

On my day off, I rushed into City Lit eager to cultivate a career as a book writer rather than a bookseller. 'Finding Your Voice' was run by an Irish author I had never heard of. Our class was held in a garret-like room on the rooftop of Citylit in Holborn. Outside, pigeons strutted and brooded. Inside, students strutted and brooded.

The Irish author did her best to knock us into shape. We did writing exercises instead of stretches. A sentence pushed out like a lunge. Syntax instead of squats. I balanced two mixed metaphors across my shoulders before they dropped like dumbbells to the floor. The pigeons cooed. The class clapped. The Irish author introduced me to other authors I had never heard of.

'What are you reading?' Mickey asked one night in bed.

I held up a book of Raymond Carver's short stories.

'More mouldy old depressing stuff,' Mickey said.

Those early years in London were full of the mouldy old depressing stuff. I was exasperated by everything. Our poverty. Mum's cancer scare. When Mickey was down he listened to the music of Damien Dempsey. Damien was also Irish but unlike Mickey he was not very funny. When I was down Mickey sometimes joked, 'Has the little Kiwi been taking its special pills?'

I refused to go on anti-depressants. Instead I sought refuge in books. I related to the anecdote about Raymond Carver standing in a laundromat waiting for his kids' clothes to dry and realising that his life did not resemble that of any of his literary heroes. I didn't marry young like Raymond Carver or have any children, but I had once waited in a laundromat in Kentish Town for my clothes to dry. On top of a huge industrial drier was a hamster in a cage. The hamster was a tawny shade of ginger. I loaded my wash into the drier and pushed a coin in the slot. Clunk. The hamster span around the wheel in its cage. My clothes whirled. I sat on the bench of the laundromat, reading *What We Talk About When We Talk About Love.*

'What if our marriage doesn't work out?' I asked Mickey.

'Then it will make a good chapter for the autobiography,' he said.

In London we moved in and out of rented flats. Dalston. Stoke Newington. Stamford Hill. Our bills arrived addressed to new postcodes. Mickey left Borders Charing Cross Road. I stayed on at Borders Islington. Mickey worked nights in hospitality. Our shifts were often out of sync. I wanted to be a writer; Mickey wanted to be an actor. We pursued our separate goals with ardour.

At Borders Islington I started co-writing a satirical romance called *The Borders of Love* with a fellow employee. Saul was crudite and witty. He prevailed over the main information desk like an intellectual Yul Brunner. He was also the only Borders staff member who could get away with referring to Starbucks as a coffee emporium over the in-store tannoy. Saul and I wrote a few pages of *The Borders of Love* together under my porn name (Sooty O'Donahue)* before the story evaporated like the froth of a Starbucks cappuccino.

Meanwhile I had graduated from 'Finding your voice' and moved on to 'Narrative Drive'. The new class met at the Dalston Library on the Number 30 bus route to Hackney Wick. I walked to lessons each week past the overland station and the Dalston market. Pale chickens hung from the awning of stalls, feet still attached, necks broken. I glanced through windows at greasy spoon cafés, Turkish restaurants and the wooden veneers of local pubs. 'Ricky! Ricky!' EastEnders elbowed and dodged one another on the street. The red double-decker buses docked at the lights, their engines generating exhaust.

'Narrative Drive' was run by a Grenadan author called Jacob Ross. The group was composed of middle-aged women all ready to strike flint from the tinderbox. Jacob began our weekly sessions with a new workout. He set the timer on his watch. 'When I say go, start writing. Then I am going to call out a sequence of words, as I call out each word I want you to incorporate it seamlessly into the sentence you are writing.'

The middle-aged women and I looked at one another.

'Go,' Jacob said.

Sooty arrived at work and went STRAIGHT down to THE basement.

In THE sort room the inventory processing team were FIERCE at work on three LUMBERING pallets, like A herd of cardboard RHINOS waiting to be tamed.

---

* To work out your own porn name combine the name of your first pet and your mother's maiden name – e.g., Sooty was a little grey kitten I owned when I was ten.

In the sort room Sooty PERCIEVED a dummies guide on salamanders that had been binced WRONG for the SEX section.

'Guys!' she scolded. 'Retail IS detail.'

THE IPT team grunted AND kept shelving AND grunting. At least they weren't SEVERELY flouting the staff handbook again by CONNECTING in dangerous horseplay. 'ONIONS!' Sooty cursed, she didn't understand how the IPT team couldn't be more FERVENT about their work. Forget the LOW pay, LOW status and REPETITION. Selling STUFF. And REPETITION. That was what she lived for. She even loved the NAUTICAL theme that had been used to CHIRPILY label the instore fixtures SO that the tall bookshelves were KNOWN as bays and the LOW bookshelves as gondalas, but the FLANKS of each bookshelf were simply CHRISTENED endcaps. Sooty loved sailing the EARTH, stocking the bays with the SPANKING new bestsellers. She was the kind of GIRL who could merchandise the HELL out of an end cap and still have VIM to redesign a till queue at the end of the day.

'HORSERADISH!' She was going TO get that supervisor promotion if it FLAGGELATED her.

Filling her trolley was KAPUT so she scanned the sort room, her GAPE gliding over the rows of blue clad industrial shelving

'Hey, what's this?' she walked over to a HANDSOME box in the corner.

The IPT guys GESTICULATED non-commitally. 'Must be a NEW-FANGLED sideline for the till queue.'

Sooty REVIEWED the invoice. 'Can YOU guys get a binc sticker on this right away. I need to sell it CURRENTLY. Truck to the floor in 24!'

The mechanical hound waited in the dark. Its eight HAUNCHES packed into a STYROFOAM base. The hound's proboscis was INSERTED inside its muzzle. The HATCH opened. A RAY of florescent light. The mechanical *hound OGLED the girl FLOATING above its face like a SYMBOL. Its eyes glowed MINT green.*

The timer went off.

Day 12: Every word was torture, let alone every word count. I knew nothing about hounds, not even mechanical hounds. I didn't have a dog. What did a proboscis look like? Why couldn't I be a normal person?

The timer went off.

In 2004 in a small flat above Stoke Newington High Street I picked up the phone. A mirror of a pock-marked moon, straddled by black branches hung on the wall. Bring-Bring. The dull sound of ringing on the flip side of the world. Outside, the real moon was only a sliver away from full.

'Hello?' His voice was gruff, no nonsense.

'Dad, it's me.'

'Are you all right?'

A small voice from London, bogged down with poverty and shame. 'No.'

'What is it? What's going on there?'

Our apartment on Stoke Newington High Street was awash with yellow streetlight, shadows stretched across the laminated floor. The fridge hummed a mechanical tune and the digital clock in the kitchen blinked back the seconds and minutes. Mint-green. Our bedroom was empty, the duvet flung back on my side. The vats behind the downstairs bar whirred.

'Mickey hasn't come home,' I said.

Static crackled down the line. Dad sighed.

It was not the first time.

'Do you know where he is?'

'No,' I said.

'What's the time in London?' Dad asked.

'It's quarter past four. I know he's probably just out drinking, but I can't stop worrying.'

'It's a shame he's like this,' Dad said.

'He fell asleep on a bus once,' I said. 'He called me disorientated because he didn't know where he was. But what if he isn't drunk and something's happened to him and he's been beaten up or killed or in an accident and I don't even know?'

I started to cry and then I felt bad for crying and for calling too.

'I wish you were closer,' Dad said.

'Me too.' My tears tasted of salt. I imagined the tide coming in along Lyall Bay beach, the sand building up in the brick drive and the sound of the planes landing and taking off. The seagulls' white neck ruffs ruffled by southerlies.

'I miss you, Dad.'

'I miss you, too.'

Dad talked about how hard it is to make a relationship work with no money, no time together, both of us working different shifts, dissatisfied in ourselves and in our lives.

'You better try and get some sleep,' Dad said.

After I hung up the phone, my legs were stiff from sitting on the floor. Pins and needles rushed up and down my calves. I wandered to the bread bin and carved off a sliver of soft white Turkish bread. Then tried Mickey's mobile one last time. 'Hi, I can't get to the phone right now. So please leave a message.' His voice sounded bouncing and buoyant.

Their marriage was an elastic band that had lost its pull. They lay in bed. Spine to spine. The cameras rolled. Oskar Werner turned his head in his sleep and Julie Christie pulled the duvet closer around her shoulders. Day 13 and I was watching the film again. Oskar was trapped in a bad dream. So was I. Memories rewound: nights in bed beside Mickey like two books side by side on a shelf. 'Mind the gap,' the voice on the London tube always said.

On screen the arched tracks of a railway rushed past. Again and again. The cinemotographer Nicholas Roeg shot the footage of the empty tracks for the nightmare sequence. Oskar tossed and turned, slack mouthed in his sleep, he groaned. In his nightmare Julie wore a dowdy nana cardigan and a string of pearls. She struck a match. All around her the books were burning. Julie smiled, like a Borders employee, one that was happy to help. How had she wound up married to Mickey Romance?

Their honeymoon took place a year overdue. They went to Nerja, a small seaside town in the Costa-Del-Sol. Out of season. The sun sparkled on the Mediterranean sea. The light was crisp. Nerja rocked back and forth; the town rebuilt on the surface of the sea. They did the touristy things that honeymooners do. Gelato, tapas, beer. Locals hung their laundry from out of white windows. Towels and sheets kicked in the breeze. A Frank Sinatra lookalike lip-synced in the square. Oscar took photographs of the stray cats that populated the beach. At night they ate paella and watched the sun set. He ordered Long Island Ice Teas and paid for them by credit card.

The houses above the beach were white and unknown. They walked along the shore in bare feet, the sand swirled around their toes as dusk rushed in. He picked up a seashell. Specks of sand on his fingers, beneath his thumbnail. The wind whipping close enough to move the hairs on his wrists. The shell was a spiral, a unicorn's horn. The turret had once housed a sea creature, something unknown and unseen, now long gone.

A fat seagull rode the wind above their heads, zig-zagging on its currents.

He gave the shell to her, she closed her palm around it and carried it along the beach. His arm loose around her shoulders. The stray cats darted in and out of the boats along the sand. One slept in the tarpaulin. She drew her jumper close around her neck as the wind picked up. The hem of the sea ran over her toes.

He found a sand dune, protected from the wind. They put back on their shoes and socks. He took the bottle of wine out of his long coat and uncorked it. She set down two plastic cups.

'A toast,' he said.

She raised her cup and held the hair back from her eyes.

'To us,' he said.

Beads of sand on their lips as they drank. 'Let's stay up all night and talk about our childhoods,' he said. One of their jokes.

'You were flirting with the waitress tonight.'

He poked her. 'Don't be jellybags.'

The seagull was gone now, but they could hear its sharpened cries in the skies above. The sea rushing and hushing, charging, then dissolving, a wedding train evaporating on the sand.

She set her plastic cup down in the cold, dense dune.

'I don't want to go back home tomorrow,' she said.

'I know.' His shadow stretched over hers. Their teeth clinked like glasses in a fumbled toast. His lips tasted of wine, the scratch of his chin against her face. Rough. The desolation of love swept through her. Then an image of Frank Sinatra crooning in the square.

Sometimes love doesn't return from a Ryanair holiday. In the morning Julie slipped the seashells into her ears and heard waves breaking. Their flight accelerated along the tarmac and she remembered the seagull, wings extended, just riding the fluctuations in the current.

In 1966 in the cutting room on the set of Pinewood studios film editor Thom Noble superimposed Julie Christie's face over Oskar's using a 24 second dissolve. On screen Oscar's nightmare had climaxed. The pixels evaporated. One face into the next. It was another Hitchcock reference, this time to *The Wrong Man*.

The timer went off.

Day 14. I got up at 6.30am and set the timer on my iPhone. Word count: 9,905. I could do it. I could still finish NaNoWriMo. I just had to stay focused. When I was with Mickey I had been sent to an anxiety workshop at Homerton hospital. During the workshop I had been given a list of the different types of change that can happen to a person in a year. I had to circle the types of change that had happened to me. I stared at the list and then at the fire hydrant fixed to the hospital wall, its black nozzle awaiting a hypothetical emergency.

I closed my eyes and imagined Julie Christie on the set of Truffaut's *Fahrenhiet 451*. She was all dressed up with nowhere to go. I started to type. Linda took the tube into the city, got out and entered a tall mirrored high rise. She rode the elevator to the thirteenth floor – ping – walked out along the corridor and opened an innocuous office door. She seemed to know where she was going which was good because I wasn't sure. We were way off Truffaut's script and in unchartered territory that had never even been covered in Bradbury's novel.

'I'm concerned, Linda.' The psychiatrist office swung around in his swivel chair, holding a list in one hand and a stress ball in the other. The stress ball was merchandised to look like a golden snitch.

'I just need my special pills,' Linda said.

In my mind she looked like a desperate housewife. On the set of *Fahrenhiet 451*, Truffaut had requested she was styled like Carole Lombard. Whoever the hell Carole Lombard was.*

'Are you going to give me a new prescription or not?' my Linda demanded.

I decided *my* Linda didn't like men in power; maybe, like me, she'd even worked briefly (but memorably) in the sex industry, as a receptionist answering the phones at a 'high-class' massage parlour. 'Femme Fatale Linda speaking. How can I help?' It was impossible to say what her backstory was as neither Bradbury or Truffaut had ever said it. All the embers were burning.

'I'm beginning to wonder if the pills aren't masking the real problem?' The psychiatrist said. He might have looked like the counseller who took the class at Homerton Hospital, if only I could remember him as clearly as the fire hydrant.

Of course they were masking the real problem! That's why she needed more.

'I think we should talk about your husband,' he said.

Linda looked at the paperweight of the Twin Towers on his desk.

'My husband thinks I watch too much TV.' She got out of her seat and walked over to the window. Outside, the real towers shimmered in the late afternoon sunshine or perhaps they glistened in the early morning rain. She thought briefly about

---

* Lombard obviously weighted more heavily in the male psyche of the era than she does now. Julie Christie however... that hair!

history; fires that had burned and fires that had been put out. And where there was fire: smoke. I decided her overdose had been an accident. Her husband was working late so she'd popped a pill and watched TV. Popped a pill. Her house, filled with canned laughter. So what if she wore seashells to help her sleep? When her music washed up on the pillow her husband told her it sounded like tinnitus. He never asked what she listened to. Never asked what she watched on TV. Never asked about her family.

'It can be hard to keep emotionally present in a relationship over time,' the psychiatrist said. He passed Linda the list.

She stared at it and then at the fire hydrant fixed to the wall, its black nozzle awaiting a hypothetical emergency.

'Would you like to hold the stress ball?'

Linda nodded. The ball was soft and warm. She squeezed it.

'How's your sex life?' he asked.

The timer went off.

Day 15. In the evening I lay on the couch drinking red wine and reading *Fahrenheit 451*. Word count: totally wasted. My boyfriend careened around a corner in *Grand Theft Auto* and crashed into a pedestrian.

'Shit,' I put the book down.

'What?'

'Clarisse is killed in a car accident.'

'Who's Clarisse?'

'How could I have missed such an important detail?'

'Do you want a refill?' My boyfriend held up the bottle of red.

Truffaut had changed the ending. In the film Clarisse escapes society and is reunited with Montag when he flees the city to live among the book people. But Ray Bradbury killed Clarisse – and even mentioned her death in the introduction to *Fahrenheit 451*. He said that Truffaut's film gave her a longer life – which, at the time, he considered a mistake.

Later, Bradbury had a change of heart. When he wrote *Fahrenheit 451* for the theatre (he was nothing if not prolific) he let Clarisse live. Although he never agreed with Truffaut's decision to make her a grown woman instead of a teenager. His Clarisse represented innocence. She taught Montag, the fireman, what it meant to be free. Yeah. *Free of his wife*, I thought. Bradbury wrote about Clarisse as though her innocence could be maintained across a life time. But innocence has a use-by date like everything else.

I'd read this introduction several times yet I'd completely glossed over Clarisse's death. Too much wine.

The next morning I sat back down at my desk. I'd come to a hole in the story. The narrative arc was unravelling. I was sweating. I wiped my forehead. Letters pooled on my fingertips like alphabet soup. Clarisse was a composition made out of thin air. Her story was a loose thread. If I let go she'd disappear.

I turned to SparkNotes and had a crack at another essay question. What was the importance of Clarisse in Bradbury's novel? For me: zilch. However, the importance of Julie Christie playing the part of Clarisse seemed increasingly critical.

Writing for the *New York Times* critic Bosley Crowther deemed her portrayal of Clarisse 'a bleakly defeminized version' of the 'elegant, sexy wife who doesn't care beans for reading and gets all her information from watching the wall-to-wall television screen.'

Bosley was right. At best Christie's Clarisse deserved a B minus. But at least her haircut was always an A plus.

In 1965 Christie was in Madrid finishing up on the set of *Doctor Zhivago*. The producer Lewis M. Allen and Truffaut flew out to visit her.

Originally Truffaut asked her to play one part in *Fahrenheit 451*. Julie said, 'Oui.'

The financing for the film came together quickly. In *The Making of Fahrenheit 451* the film's producer Lewis Allen confessed the financing wasn't due to the director or even the script. Julie had just won an Academy Award for her work in *Darling*. She was hot shit.

'The parts weren't very good individually,' Lewis said on the documentary.. He had a patient smile. Truffaut hadn't bought into Bradbury's vision of a heroine and a villainess. He thought instead of Clarisse and Mildred as two aspects of the same person. So Allen suggested Julie Christie play both parts. Eureka! Truffaut was stoked. Problem sorted.

But then Christie's ex-lover Terence Stamp pulled out of the role of Montag: Jellybags.

And Julie was exhausted after finishing *Doctor Zhivago*. (I was not surprised. I was exhausted after watching it. It was very long. And the wolves!)

The doctor prescribed bed rest. Julie arrived on set two weeks later than scheduled.

The day she finally started the trouble with Oskar began.

During their first meeting Oskar wanted to tell Christie how to play her part: *mansplaining*. Truffaut apparently liked working with Christie because she didn't ask what her motivation was. With a face like Christie's, you don't have to ask.

In one early scene Oskar felt that Christie, dressed as Clarisse, should turn and touch him.

'No,' Francois said. No touchy.

Oskar pouted. He wasn't happy and he'd try and get back at Truffaut later, using – of all things – his haircut as a weapon.

Truffaut's film wasn't about a love affair between a man and a woman; it was about a love affair with books.

I remembered a coffee mug I'd seen online recently which said 'Reading is sexy.' I wasn't sure Truffaut agreed.

The timer went off.

Day 16, Day 17, Day 18.

Sooty made her pilgrimage to work at Ogle. The retail giant tempted its employees with flexible working conditions and staff discounts. The building was shaped like an igloo. Every revolving door was an entrance or an exit. Customers flowed in and out. The eyelash in the electronic sign above the door winked. Ogle was open seven days a week until 11pm. Ogle: eyes a-goggle. Sooty arrived at work and checked the daily roster. She was stationed behind the main information desk. The mechanical hound stood next to the desk and emitted a soft internal whirring. It was recharging.

A couple approached, holding a pair of Grande lattes.

'What's that?' The man pointed at the hound.

'It's a Tinderbox,' Sooty said. 'A brand of e-reader preloaded with every Classic from the twentieth century.'

The wife put her latte down on the main information desk. 'Is it an antique?'

'Yes.' Sooty smiled. 'It comes with a reading light.'

'It has such big eyes. It looks a little freaky,' her husband said.

'The hound has five vocal options. It can read "Go The Fuck To Sleep" in the voice of Samuel L Jackson.'

'I don't think that's appropriate,' he replied.

'I don't think the price is appropriate either,' his wife inspected the sales ticket. The husband laughed. 'Not unless we win the lottery.'

The wife handed Sooty her coffee cup and the couple headed off in the direction of the toilets.

The mechanical hound turned and quoted Dostoevsky:

'Deprived of meaningful work, men and women lose their reason for existence; they go stark, raving mad.'

'Oh shut up,' Sooty said. 'You just inserted that quote for the word count.'

The timer went off.

At Borders Islington I wrote down my preferred sections on a piece of paper and submitted it to management.

- Fiction.
- Art.
- Film/TV.

I was put in charge of computers, maths and science. My worst subjects in high school.

The timer went off.

Each day at Borders resembled the next. The daily roster was divided into one- and two-hour blocks. Section. Tills. Main Info. Staff consulted the roster each hour and changed squares.

'Do you have *The Story of Pee*?' a young woman asked.

I stood before the computer at the main information desk. 'Do you know the author's name?'

'No, but it just won a prize.'

'Do you mean *The Life of Pi*?'

'That's it!'

I picked up a copy of Yann Martel's novel from the stack behind the main information desk and handed it to her.

'Thanks. It's a present for my mother.'

I thought briefly of the girl's mother soon to be united with Yann Martel's novel. A union that never would have happened had the novel not won the 2003 Booker Prize. I wondered how long Martel had spent selecting the title. I imagined The Life of Pi was more than just a summary of the novel's activity, of Pi's life, that the sound of each syllable was mysteriously complete to Martel. Yet, I also saw how the title had left the novel open to misinterpretation. The Story of Pee could have been a potted history of the customer toilets at Borders Islington.

The toilets were located on the ground floor between the start of Fiction and True Crime. The security gates beeped if a 'tagged' book passed through the entrance to the toilets. Most thieves had the presence of mind to check the inside covers of books for the white tags or 'chicklets' that set the security gates off. But not all books were tagged.

The toilets overflowed with criminal activity. Teenagers took great delight in stuffing the bowls with wadded toilet paper. Then they graffitied the doors and walls, often with their own blood and shit. Junkies left used needles lying on the floor like broken fountain pens, and the tails of used tampons dangled from the stuffed mouths of the sanitary bins.

The code for the toilet door was distributed by the staff member at the main information desk.

'The toilets are disgusting,' customers often told me.

I reserved my judgment. My threshold for disgust was high.

In 2005 the Borders Islington management team finally instigated a new toilet policy: customers had to obtain an in-store receipt to gain access to the toilets. The code for the toilets printed out at the bottom of the receipt. No purchase, no toilet. This strategy was a deterrent intended to keep out the illegitimate: bums, teenagers and drug addicts. It also kept out Jon Ronson. The author who wrote *The Men Who Stare at Goats* was not a man happy to produce a receipt to use a customer toilet. In his *Guardian* column he complained about the new customer toilets regime. He also complained about the staff member who policed the use of the toilets from the main information desk.

Customers crossed Borders Islington in currents. I collected up the driftwood once the tide had gone out and the store had closed. At Borders re-shelving was called recovery. Occasionally customers solicited my opinion. 'Is this any good?' 'Have you read this?' A book picked up, its cover turned to greet me like the face of an old friend. I gave stock answers. 'It's been very popular.' 'That's one of our bestsellers.' 'I haven't got around to that one yet, but it's on my list.' Sometimes I was honest. 'I don't know.' But my ambiguity was a repellent. Customers rarely chose a book that I could not fully endorse. Yet, how could I have read every title? How could I have been attracted to every cover? I had my own interests, my own preoccupations.

In Fiction I found an illustrated novel about the adventures of an existential cat. I spent half an hour flicking through the book instead of shelving the nearby cart of recovery. The cat was just a wistful stranger struggling to assemble the intellectual jigsaw of life. When I went relooking for the book after payday it had disappeared. Sold? Surely not. The existential cat wasn't Dan Brown. I tried countless times to relocate it to no avail. Borders was a maze. The book could have been misshelved anywhere. To make matters worse, I couldn't remember the title or the author's name. I was my own worst nightmare. A customer. I didn't even have enough information to find it on Amazon.

During my tenure at Borders I grew to hate the bestsellers. A new Jodi Picoult felt about as sincere as a cheeseburger. Take off the wrapper and the moral dilemma lay in the centre like a gherkin, ready to be digested. Then what were you hungry for? Borders revolved around the seasons. I filled Valentine's Day displays to the brim with *Purple Ronnie* mini books and sex cheques. Easter: a line of fluffy chicks from Paperchase. I liked to decorate the tables with gift cards and other items of quirk. The shopper is a magpie. Mother's Day: more pink, more pastels, more chick lit, more Jodi (is there any occasion Jodi cannot rise to?). Father's Day: men and their sheds, a book of knitted socks, Dita Von Teese's *Burlesque and the Art of the Teese*. Halloween, then stocking fillers:

Eats, Shoots, and Leaves
Why Don't Penguins Feet Freeze?
Victorian Do's and Don'ts for Wives (and Husbands)
The tills chimed. Santa came. Then he went.

Sex: always over stimulated. Paper cut-outs from the pop-up Karma Sutra torn asunder. *The Story of O* my god, why is this section such a fucking mess? One day I caught a rare glimpse of some customers browsing the sex section. A group of teenage boys flicked to a large graphic image and asked, 'Have you done this?'

I didn't reply. But I had.

The timer went off.

Each writing day resembled the next. I got up, checked my NaNoWriMo word count, opened my laptop – ping! – and typed: a fireman twirled down the pole as gracefully as a stripper. He alighted and tipped his hat.

'You're awake. How do you feel?'

The blonde teenager in my Word document sat up. 'Where am I?' she asked, her pulse quickening.

On the wall above her head was the fireman's motto. 'We burn, so that you don't have to.'

'You're a clever girl, aren't you?' The fire chief stood by her single bed. (I wondered if he was Captain Beatty, although he looked a bit like the Irish manager at Borders Islington.)

'I'm not that bright. My math is terrible,' the blonde said. (I wondered if she was Clarisse although her outline felt a little... sketchy.)

The fire chief produced a piece of paper from his pocket. 'Do you recognise this?'

She shook her head. 'Am I under arrest?'

'Liar,' he scoffed. 'I believe you've been given access to the world of literature, I believe you're writing your own story and that's why I had to bring you in to the station – to reel you in.'

The blonde swung her legs over the edge of the bed, it was just a cot really. The room was lined with hooks that she assumed must be for fire retardant uniforms. And for the hard shiny helmets the firemen wore on their heads. A table stood in the corner of the room, in its centre an empty ashtray and a packet of Redheads.

'Is it true?' The chief struck a match and lit up a cigarette.

'What difference does it make if I am?' she said, noticing a calander of firemen on the wall, open on Mr November. He brandished a long hose in his hands.

The chief gave her a sideways grin. 'Your prioritisation of your self is not unique. You seem to think you are special. And specialness is something we have to stub out. Our lives are waste not want not. What have you got to say that hasn't been said before? We have to recycle before we can create. That's the logic of our lives now. There are already millions of stories, and of course there are only really seven plots.'

'I thought there was only one plot.' The blonde got off the bed. Her face wasn't fragile like milk crystal and her white dress didn't whisper because she was wearing jeans.

'Ha!' The chief laughed again. 'Only one story and what would that be?'

'The fall from grace.'

She chopped him in the nuts. Those after-school Judo lessons had finally paid off.

Day 19, 1966. On the set of Pinewood studios the fire engine sailed past the window of the cutting room. The engine was designed to look like a child's toy. Its arrival on screen was accompanied by the dinky tinkle of xylophones.

Thom Noble would never think about the xylophone the same way again. He wasn't just the film's editor, he was also Truffaut's go-between. And Bernard Herrmann was not the kind of composer who welcomed second-hand instructions. Especially, 'No xylophones!'*

Noble turned and looked at Truffaut. Another day, another problem to be resolved.

Francois flicked his fingers: the movement still wasn't *fluid* enough.

On screen, Oskar clumsily donned the asbestos helmet and gloves. He looked like a bee keeper. Someone who could get down on someone else's buzz. He took the flame thrower and gingerly aimed it at the small pile of books tossed on a wire rack, as though it was a BBQ. The cast of extras gathered around the pyre.

---

* Truffaut thought Herrmann's use of the xylophone was 'too jokey'. But in the end Herrmann won out. The xylophones stayed and add to the childish tone of peril.

Francois bit his thumbnail. Oskar should have mentioned he was afraid of fire before he accepted the part. The man was an ass. His success on *Ship of Fools* had ruined him.

'Francois,' Thom queued the new take in reverse motion.

The director watched.

This time the movements were deft, smooth, assured. The helmet slipped over the actor's head. Good. The last thing Truffaut needed to see was Oskar's smiling mug. Then the gloves. The actor gripped the flamethrower: fire blazed from the hole, the books were engulfed.

'I reversed the film,' Thom said.

Truffaut clasped his shoulder. Their bromance was smouldering. So were the books.

'And it's another reference,' Thom told him.

Francois raised an eyebrow.

'To Cocteau,' Thom said. The French director Jean Cocteau had used the technique to good effect in his films.* In Cocteau's *Beauty and the Beast* (1946) one character walks up to a fire and appears to pluck a piece of paper straight out of it.

'Tres bein.' Truffaut smiled in the dark. Sparks were flying.

The timer went off.

---

* Although you can have too much of a good thing: critics were later to complain that the use of reverse motion had become endemic in Cocteau's work; an auteur's tic. Poor Jean. Shamed like the beast.

One night shift at Borders Islington the alarm on the ground floor went off just after 8pm and a bum stumbled out of the fire doors in a brown corduroy suit.

'What were you doing?' I asked. 'That area is for staff only.'

'I need the bathroom.' His eyes spiralled around the store. He was shit faced. I could have lit his breathe with a match.

'The toilets are over there.' I pointed at the large prominent sign nearby.

He shambled off towards it. I shook my head.

Time stilled on the night shift.

Downstairs in the staff room, I waited for my ready meal to heat. The plate span around inside the microwave drawn by its centrifugal pull.

I poked at my teabag with a teaspoon; it turned over in the Borders mugs like a stray water-wing.

Music seeped through the tinny speaker in the staff room.

I blew on the tea; the tanned water rippled. The table in the staff room was covered with old *Heat* magazines. Brad Pitt had left Jennifer Aniston.

'Poor Jen,' Pawla the Polish bookseller sat opposite me, stirring her tea.

'Do you really think he's having an affair with Angelina Jolie?'

'Of course.' Pawla had long spiral hair like a gypsy. When it came to matters of the heart her advice was never less than sage.

We inspected the photographs of Brad and Angelina on the set of their latest film. They leaned over a railing between takes, smiling. The borders of love can easily be breached.

A drip grew on the gnarled lip of the tap above the kitchen sink like a bungee jumper, finally let go and plunged over the edge.

The microwave beeped. I got up and peeled the shrink-wrap off.

Over the in-store tannoy the new Irish general manager announced the latest in-store specials: 'Please ask a member of staff for more details.'

'I like his accent,' I said.

Pawla raised an eyebrow. 'I bet you do.'

'What happens next in your book?' she asked.

'The lead character has an affair with the boss,' I said.

Pawla laughed.

After dinner, I chose a grey V-cart from the line up along the staff corridor. I glanced at the map which depicted the staff assembly point in case of fire. Cartoon flames gushed from the square that represented Borders Islington. I had drawn the map. But there were no fires at Borders Islington in the time I worked there. Instead, the toilets in the cinema above the store often overflowed and water dripped through the ceiling tiles. Books damaged by flood rather than fire.

I steered my empty V-cart towards the sort room.

A poster of a romance novel cover adorned one wall: Touch Not The Cat. A mountain cat sat in the centre of the poster. A man in a kilt with Fabio-flung hair rested one gentle hand on the cat – the one that was not to be touched. The book was written by Tracey Fobes, I doubted any of the staff had ever read it, but it was a talisman of great personal amusement to us. The author's vision of the world was undoubtedly more smouldering than mine.

The lift doors opened on the first floor. Computers was located in the corner. Its one highlight: a vertical window that looked out over Sainsbury's and a small stretch of road. I shelved, pausing every now and then to stare at the red-bricked wall of Sainsbury's or to follow that short stretch of road into the black volume of another London night. On the back of each book was a binc sticker that contained a code for the section. I consulted the code, then placed the book into its approximate order in the bay. Shelving produced a deep state of intellectual fatigue. In the Mind Body Spirit section the books bore titles like: *Who am I? How did I get here? Where am I going to?* In Computers the books bore titles like *Dreamweaver 5* and *Java SE7 Programming*.

I plugged away at the V-cart. An abandoned Verde Grande Starbucks coffee cup lay tipped over on an empty shelf. Milk had dried onto the wooden veneer; a trace of someone else's orgasmic day.

At the end of the shift a buzz came through on my walkie talkie.

'Megan, meet me out the back of the fire doors on the ground floor, ' the manager said. But it wasn't a lover's trist that awaited me.

'What is it?' I arrived on the scene.

'Look.' The manager pointed at the steaming pile of shit on the floor.

I covered my mouth. 'I know who did this.'

The timer went off.

Day 20. I woke up at 6.30am. Opened my MacBook Air. Checked my word count. Checked my emails. Logged into Facebook. Paused to check Twitter.

'You're not Facebooking again, are you?' my boyfriend asked.

'It's not a crime,' I said.

There was so much of *Fahrenheit 451* left. The sand was falling through the sieve but I still hadn't moved beyond 'The Hearth and the Salamander.'

'What about the false logic of Montag's boss, Captain Beatty?' my inner critic asked. 'And the old world values of Professor Faber? You haven't attempted to address either of these important characters yet.'

I knew Faber's character was named after the publishing house. But I hadn't known that Montag was named after a paper-manufacturing company. I'd read every entry on Clarisse and Mildred in SparkNotes, but I hadn't paid any attention to the male character summaries.

I turned to the in-depth analysis of Captain Beatty. Beatty was described as a complex character full of contradictions. In Bradbury's novel Beatty was the chief of the fire station. The upshot: no one ever likes the boss. I had worked under several Borders general managers and they were all fatally flawed as well. Borders Islington in particular had a reputation for burning general managers out.

The first GM went on sick leave and never came back. My predominant memory is watching him frenetically shuffle the edges of the 3-for-2 tables. The second general manager was a rogue Irishman* who'd once appeared on a British Reality TV show about his sex life. He didn't last.

In early 2005, his replacement, a high performing lesbian, stood in the lift with me, stroking her upper lip. 'You're either with me or you're against me.'

Her laser-eyes scanned the length of my V-cart.

I clutched the handle. 'I'm just trying to get this over-stock out.'

My days at Borders Islington were numbered. I had to get out. Starting with the lift. The doors pinged open and I wheeled the wobbly V-cart round the corner to the cage, swiped my staff card and sat inside, surrounded by huge rows of DVD's and CD's. The cage was black. Windowless. Discreet. Several trollies and V-carts of loose DVD and CD keepers waited nearby. The plastic keepers needed to be attached to each item of stock before it was put on the shop floor. And the DVD and CD box sets that didn't fit inside the keepers needed to be shrink-wrapped. The heat gun sat on the desk waiting for me to fire it up. There were a number of tasks I could have been doing. How could the general manager prove I was doing none of them?

I put on a Cat Stevens CD and sat in the dark eating a Starbucks chocolate muffin and crying. Out on the shop floor the shrink-age was shrinking. The clock ticking. The tills beeping.

---

* He had a cameo in *The Borders of Love* as my character Sooty's love interest, but he didn't last long in that role either.

Later I found out that she had the cage under 24-hour surveillance. One morning the police arrived and arrested two staff members from the multimedia section who had been stealing DVD's and CD's. The staff had removed the chicklet security tags and keepers in the cage, smuggled the stock out of the store and sold it on Ebay.

At the time, I was the multimedia supervisor.

The timer went off.

SPARKNOTES ESSAY QUESTION:

Why does Captain Beatty hate books?

Day 21. I logged into NaNoWriMo and checked my word count against the collective word count of the pack. Shit. I turned back to the first page of Bradbury's novel.

It was a pleasure to shrink-wrap.

It was a special pleasure to see things enveloped, packaged and changed. With the plastic heat gun in her grip, with this feisty salamander licking its warm tongue upon the world, the Starbucks Latte gurgled in her stomach, and her hands were the hands of some fantastical fireman extinguishing all the shrinkage in all the stores in the company's brief but memorable history. With her symbolic lanyard labelled 'Happy to Help' dangling around her neck, and her eyes all woozy with the thought of what came next, she flicked the switch and the plastic polymer shrivelled tight around the corners of the DVD boxset and clung to it like processed cheese. She worked in a funnel of fumes. She wanted above all to consolidate the bottom line, so that she got that promotion and the tiny raise it represented. Clunk. Holes burst in the plastic like craters and ripples cascaded across the cover of the boxset.

Sooty frowned the demonic frown of all retailers singed and driven mad by shrink-wrap.

She'd held the heat gun too close, screwed up again. Later, going to sleep in her apartment next to the whirring air vents of the shop next door, she would feel that frown gripped by her forehead muscles in the dark. It never went away, as long as she remembered.

The timer went off.

Day 22. In the morning I woke from surly dreams I couldn't remember, plunged the coffee and walked to my desk. It felt as though Bradbury and Truffaut were standing behind me, each with a hand on my shoulder. I checked my NaNoWriMo word count: 14,403.

In my word document Bradbury's character Clarisse was now dressed in a white suit and a neck ruff. I typed: *The wh23aqWQite clown picked up the light blue belt in her dressing room and regarded it as though it was a ????*

'Merde,' Truffaut said. In one of his scenes he'd used actress and stunt woman Gillian Aldam to fell a male opponent using Judo. The footage only lasted seconds; Christie and Werner watched the judo match on TV in their living room. I stared out the window of my study at the light sparkling on the waves in the harbour. The Pacific rolled in and out. A cruise ship cut across my field of vision. Truffaut watched the ship, 'je ne comprends pas?'

Truffaut was also a man of the written word. He started out as a film critic for *Cahiers du Cinema*, a highbrow French language film magazine. Apparently his criticism could be lacerating. I had a feeling he'd get on with my father. I wasn't so sure about Bradbury.

In the opening scene of Truffaut's F451 an old woman was set alight inside her library. The books in flames were handpicked by Truffaut. *Cahiers du Cinema*. A burning Spanish crossword puzzle book. Donleavey's *The Ginger Man*. The flames licked the edges, flowing, never ceasing. The actress Bea Duffell raised her arms in the centre of the pyre and was consumed.

I picked at my split ends.

I realised I should be providing the unique salient details that would bring the world of my novel to life. Unfortunately I couldn't be bothered. Did Truffaut or Bradbury ever have this problem?

I checked BrainyQuotes.

'Film lovers are sick people,' said Truffaut.

True. I did feel a bit sick, but it could just be the coffee.

In *The Making of F451* the producer Lewis Allen said they were asked to check the copyright of all the books burned in this scene and get permission from the publishers, but they never did.

I hadn't asked for permission to use *Fahrenheit 451* either. I wasn't going to sweat the small stuff.

Besides, didn't Bradbury say there were worse crimes than burning books?

Fahrenheit 451 was still lying on my desk. Unread. Although at least I'd watched the movie.

Leaves danced in front of my eyes like tears. Why was I trying to rewrite a classic I couldn't even be bothered to read? 'Life has more imagination than we do.' It was Truffaut. He pressed his hand down on my shoulder and gave it a squeeze, that's when I realised it wasn't Truffaut or even Bradbury's advice I needed to hear. I wanted to know what BrainyQuote my own father would say to me.

'What were you doing when you were my age?' I asked Dad, after I moved back to New Zealand.

'I suppose I was doing much the same thing as you.'

His two Russian wolfhounds lay on opposing couches and looked at us. They had long elegant snouts. In his thirties Dad used to drive cross-country selling books to libraries.

After Borders UK collapsed in December 2009 I had returned to Wellington to be close to Dad. His house is a jenga stack of books opposite the beach at Lyall Bay. Outside, seagulls watch the planes take off and land. At night the aluminium fence along the side of the house rattles back and forth. And the planes sound like they might crash and explode. Southerlies tear at the fence and sand beaches itself in dunes down the length of his brick driveway.

Dad has spent hours sweeping the sand from the drive. He sometimes fills a wheelbarrow and returns the sand to the beach, but it always comes back, swept in from the sea. The seagulls strut back and forth on the sea wall. The wind slices between their feathers, turns their white necks into ruffs.

I hadn't grown up with Dad, but I had spent holidays at Lyall Bay. When I opened each book I could smell time, like a dried flower, pressed between the pages. Many of Dad's books were second-hand. Their spines clothed in jackets long since faded from fashion. Tall hardbacks, buckled paperbacks, their pages well-thumbed. I used to wonder how Dad could have read so many books. Yet Dad was always reading, his nose like the prow of a ship setting out to sea. He's not like stereotypical Kiwi fathers who watch rugby and drink beer on weekends. Dad's colours were blue and grey and his silences were this colour too, because with reading there's always silence.

Dad would sit on the floor, a mug of tea at his side. Every now and then his arm would extend towards the cup and he would lift it to his lips and sip without his eyes ever leaving the page. Sunlight fell across the carpet, while I lay on the floor with the cat and watched dust rain through the air like confetti.

Each book was a porthole into another world and I imagined what it would be like to be one of the characters trapped inside.

One school holiday I wrote a short story called *The Forgotten Child*. It was about a waif waiting for a train at the station. I illustrated the story with forlorn drawings of the waif in ballpoint pen. She looked a bit like the Little Match Girl.

I showed the story to Dad.

His verdict: 'Melodramatic.'

I was 11-years-old. The waif was roughly the same age. I snuffed the memory of the Little Match Girl out. And I was alone again. Just a woman in a room trying to write. The past flickered, burned.

The timer went off.

The Borders of Love

They browsed the long afternoon through while the cold November rain fell from the sky on the roof of the store. The rain fell, the pages turned and the Starbucks coffee machine frothed. It felt as though the browsing would never stop.

They sat on red vinyl chairs and footstools in the aisles. Grande and Vente piles of magazines beside them. Countless rims of coffee buckled the pages of *Heat*. Ruffled *Women's Days* were evacuated at the end of each shift only to be reshelved. Celebrities' faces puckered with spilt milk.

It was Borders policy to allow the customers to read freely and read freely they did. Toddlers flew across the galaxy carpet in the children's section and shook books from the Mr Men spinner while baby buggies blocked the aisles and hardbacks swung ajar from their spines. The picture book section was scratched and sniffed, its pop ups decanted onto the floor.

'Do you have another copy?' The customer at the till mooed at me. I wondered who she thought had destroyed the existing copy. It was never the staff. It was the browsers.

After the closure of Borders US, one customer lamented in a newspaper article that it was the best place for meeting friends and grazing the written word.

In the 1970s Tom and Louis Borders opened the first store in Ann Arbour, Michigan. The brothers began by selling second-hand textbooks but quickly branched into new stock. After short stays in other downtown locations they moved into a two-story, 10,000-square-foot storefront – a former men's clothing store that dated back to the nineteenth century – on State Street. Borders Store 1 remained at this address until it was liquidated. Tom managed the store and in the age before personal computers Louis Borders pioneered an inventory system on three-inch punch cards. His approach grew into a separate business: Book Inventory Systems. *Sexy.*

Borders was originally founded on range. Staff knew their shit. They managed their own sections. They bought their own stock. It was a really big bookstore. And it was good.

The second store popped up in the mid-80s in Birmingham, Michigan, about an hour's drive from Ann Arbour. Then the third in Atlanta, and the fourth in Indianapolis. Apparently Store 1's long time manager Joe Gable used to toast the staff on New Year's Eve with champagne. The good times were flowing.

By the time the Borders Brothers sold the chain to Kmart in 1992 there were twenty-one Borders stores. Borders spread to the UK, Australasia and Singapore. At its peak the Borders Group operated over 1,200 stores worldwide. When I started at Store 505 in 2002 Borders had a deal with Amazon. If a book was unavailable at Borders we recommended the customer purchase it direct from Amazon. Jeff Bezos was building an online empire he'd started in a garage in Seattle. It was all a matter of adopting the right long-term strategy.

By 2002, the Borders brand had eroded. It no longer meant quality and range. Now it just meant the middle of the road.

Bestsellers:

CD: Norah Jones.

QP: *The Da Vinci Code*.

DVD: *Lost in Translation*.

'There was no better place for grazing the written word and for meeting the best of friends.'

Tom is now an investor based in Austin, Texas. Louis, who founded the dot-com firm Webvan, is based in northern California.

The timer went off.

In the second section of Bradbury's *Fahrenheit 451* – 'The Sieve and the Sand' – Montag makes Mildred sit on the floor while he recites quotations from literature. Forced reading is never pleasant.

'The Sieve and the Sand' also refers to Montag's childhood memory of trying to fill a sieve with sand on the beach – to earn a dime from a cousin – and crying at the futility of the task. Montag compares this memory to his attempt to read the Bible as fast as possible on the subway in the hope that, if he reads fast enough, some of the material will stay in his memory.

I was by now speeding through *Fahrenheit 451* as fast as possible. It wasn't staying in my memory either. Every time I turned back to the novel I was surprised by how alien it seemed. If the book was written now there'd be questions about why Mildred didn't leave Montag earlier, but as it was written in the 1950s I assumed economic stability played a strong part in her decision. Who else but her husband could buy her that second wall screen?

Part of me felt sorry for Mildred. Why? I'm a passionate – nay an ardent reader – yet, as my experience of re-reading Bradbury's *Fahrenheit 451* deepened, I realised I was rooting for the villain. I blamed the film, and Truffaut. To gaze at Julie Christie playing Linda, dressed in her creamy white twin set, was to project onto a shallow screen. I imagined myself as Linda, looking like Julie, crouched on the kitchen floor, listening to my husband reading aloud. Linda's biggest crime was watching Reality TV.

I put down the book and started to type.

'Women lure you in with sex but then the sex dries up,' I wrote, attributing the quote to Montag. It seemed like something he might have said. Or maybe it just seemed like something Julie Christie might have heard, on the set of Truffaut's *Fahrenhiet 451*. Or perhaps it was said to her by a disgruntled partner as it was once said to me.

I picked up my copy of Bradbury's book and checked how 'The Sieve and the Sand' began again. I had to keep my facts straight, right? In the first sentence it was November and it was raining. I was instantly reminded me of the Guns n' Roses song 'November Rain'. Axl Rose, like Bradbury, was American. Maybe it really did rain a lot there in November?

As a bookseller, reader and writer I knew I should share Bradbury's point of view that books are the highest form of art. Yet I was seriously considering the counter argument. Maybe my life would have been better off without books? I don't know if Axl Rose has read many novels, yet I defy anyone who has watched the 'November Rain' video to say life hasn't moved him deeply. Life and Stephanie Seymour. Of course it was easy to mock the aspirations of 'November Rain' from the safe distance of adulthood – but I still understood that Seymour's long tanned legs occupied a terrain at once sexually and spirtiually moving.

I bet Bradbury's Mildred also longed for a life that was epic. And for a man that had loved her as passionately as Axl had loved Stephanie.

Axl's ballad stirred my emotions. Bradbury thought books were the one true form of expression. But what about music? Songs contained words but they were more than words too. In 'November Rain' the music was torrential, the violins flashed, the symphony swept over me.

I leaned over my laptop, thinking about Bradbury. Did he ever lean over his typewriter thinking about me – not as Megan Dunn of course – or even as a New Zealander, although Americans often reach for New Zealand as some kind of hinterland on the edge of what is possible* – but as some abstract future reader? As he scratched his balls – it gets

---

*   In Michael Mann's *Heat* (1995) Robert De Niro's character – a professional thief – tells his girlfriend, 'We'll move to New Zealand'. New Zealand is offered as an escape route, a safe haven beyond the borders of America.

sweaty down there when you're cramped in a chair writing up against the timer, your bag of change growing slimmer, those dimes dying quick deaths with each spurt of sentences and paragraphs – did he ever think, hey, maybe one day someone will summarise my novel into handy bite sized chunks to aid intellectual digestion?

SPARKNOTES ESSAY QUESTION:

How plausible is the future envisioned in this novel?

The filming for *Fahrenheit 451* took place in three locations outside Pinewood studios:

1. The woods where the book people are found at the end of the film.
2. A row of modernist houses in Roehampton.
3. The monorail outside Chateauneuf, south of Paris.

The suspended monorail was designed by French Bridge builder Lucien Chadenson in 1947. The track was a test site that ran for half a mile. It was a vision of the future that never took off.

On July 7th 2005, I stood at a bus stop on Stoke Newington Church Street and thought: the winds of change are coming. A sheet of newspaper scuttled down the street to punctuate the thought. Whether it was the winds of change ruffling the paper or just a strong gust was hard to say. I had reached a point in my marriage where something had to happen. Either things were going to get better or worse.

I had applied to do my masters in creative writing at the University of East Anglia and Borders were opening a new store in Norwich. If I got a place on the masters, I could transfer to the new store and keep my job. Mickey had applied to do an acting course in London. We were both waiting to see which way the wind would blow us.

I stood in the cold, drinking my takeaway latte and waiting for the Number 73 bus. The bus stop was opposite the public library. 'Without libraries what have we? We have no past and no future,' Ray Bradbury said. I agreed. I had written my first published short story in the Stoke Newington library. The story consisted of some things that had happened to me and some things that hadn't happened to me. 'Most importantly the story was alive and you were very much in evidence in it,' Dad said. I printed out his email and kept it next to my desk.

It was still two years before the first Kindle would be released onto the market and seven years before Zadie Smith would publish 'North West London Blues', an essay about the fate of the Willesden Green Library in particular and the uncertain future of public libraries in general. 'What kind of a problem is a library?' Zadie Smith asks in that essay. 'At the extreme pole of this view is the technocrat's total faith: with every book in the world online, what need could there be for the physical reality?'

The physical reality was still firmly in place that morning. I stood at the bus stop, preparing myself for another day of book selling as opposed to book writing. I was sipping my latte at 8.50am when the first bomb went off on the Circle Line, eight minutes out of Kings Cross Station, travelling eastbound between Liverpool Street and Aldgate. The second bomb detonated less than fifty seconds later; then the third.

Calls began to come through on mobiles.

'A bomb's gone off on the tube.'

'What's happened?'

'Which tube?'

The news was not official. We were just a bunch of commuters waiting to go to work. 'Do you know what's happening?' 'Is there any more news?'

I called Mickey. At home in bed with a hangover. Safe.

'Don't worry,' he said.

The Number 73 pulled up. I stepped on board and held on to the rail that ran along the ceiling. The passengers wobbled like skittles as the bus lurched around corners. The 73 finally pulled up in Islington, a few metres shy of the Angel Tube station. The entrance was thick with commuters flowing out on to the street. I stepped off the bus.

'Another bomb's gone off,' a passenger said.

I crossed the road, feeling a sense of dread. The threat of terrorism that had hovered over London since 9/11 was in the process of being realised. I joined the other Borders supervisors and managers downstairs in the staff office. We began to phone the team on the late shift to tell them not to come in and to make sure everyone was safe. The networks had flooded. All the mobile lines were down. No one could get through.

In 1966 Oskar, Julie, Truffaut and cinematographer Nicholas Rogue journeyed to France to shoot the exterior shots of the monorail. The shoot took only two days. It was enough.

The wind blew Julie's skirt around her knees.

'Cut!' Truffaut smiled.

She smiled back. Francois seemed troubled and she wanted to get him something. A gift. But what?

Oskar kept botching his line.

'What's that number on your shoulder?' she asked.

'Oh this?'

His Germanic accent lent the role of Montag a certain frisson.

He explained that *Fahrenheit 451* is the temperature at which book paper catches fire. It was an expoistory line of dialogue for the benefit of the audience and Oskar's delivery of it was perfunctory. Julie tried to keep her stride light, breezy as she walked beside him. The role of Clarisse was hard to get to grips with. At least she had the wife down pat. Maybe it was the costume? Truffaut was so specific. The wife was to be dressed like Carole Lombard.

In between takes she watched Nicholas Rogue shoot extra footage of the track from below, its curving rail like the spine of a giant centipede. The takes on the train would be blue screened in later.

'Did you know we've been using the escape hatch,' Oskar said.

He looked pointedly at the stairs that opened from the floor of the monorail and led into the nearby paddock.

'Yes,' Julie replied. They'd been going up and down it all morning. And she was the one wearing a skirt.

'Passengers would have only used the escape hatch in case of emergency.'

'Maybe Francois thinks it adds to the vision of the future?' Julie lit up a fresh cigarette.

'But it's incorrect,' Oskar said.

The timer went off.

My favourite scenes in Truffaut's film took place on the monorail. I like train journeys because there is never any pressure to improve yourself when you travel. You are in limbo. A body suspended over the tracks, clackety clack.

In Truffaut's film Clarisse and Montag met on the monorail. Julie watched Oskar, his black glove fastened to the rail.

Strangers on a train. The rhythm of the track. Clarisse spoke to Montag. Clackety clack.

I loved the dreamy music. The monorail scenes were especially romantic – the score is by Bernard Herrmann, who was going through a messy divorce when Truffaut hired him. He'd also just been fired from *Torn Curtain* by Hitchcock. Poor Herrmann. The music on the monorail was plaintive. I bet he was someone who enjoyed a good train ride. It would have given him time to think about his wife (and Hitchcock), to wonder if there was another way things could have turned out.

Herrmann was also a book lover and a great friend of Ray Bradbury's. The tracks kept connecting and interconnecting: *Colchester, Manningtree, Needham Market, Stowmarket, Diss...*

In 2005 I sat in a booth staring at the pale outline of my own expression; I looked like an extra, someone who might not even feature in the official script. In the weeks after the July bombings, colour photocopies of Shahara Islam hung in the windows of the Cooperative Bank in Islington. Missing. Twenty-years-old. She'd worked as a teller in the bank. Fifty-two people died in the London bombings that day and Shahara Islam was one of them.

She'd stepped on to the Number 30 bus en route to Hackney Wick as it pulled into Euston Bus station. Crowds of people evacuated from the tubes were boarding buses. Mickey and

I had friends in Hackney Wick. I had taken the Number 30 many times. Shahara Islam took a seat downstairs at the back of the bus. Eighteen-year-old Hasib Hussain, the youngest suicide bomber, was sitting on the top deck at 9.47am. The timer went off.

I watched London recede, stations and platforms scattered with strangers slid from view; the council estates gave way to green fields. This was the English countryside of Kenneth Grahame's *The Wind in The Willows*. I gazed out the window half expecting to see Moley and Badger, or at least Tarka the Otter, peddling downstream.

At the University of East Anglia, I sat in the waiting room trying to size up the competition. You can't tell the quality of someone's metaphor from the colour of their cardigan, or predict their gift with plot, based on the flash of their socks or their brand of shoes. I got talking to an Indian businessman, wearing a suit. He held a briefcase on his lap. He told me he was a short story writer with a long history of publication. I was convinced he was the next Salman Rushdie.

He was interviewed first. I waited. I looked at the water cooler in the room as though it was a barometer of taste. Eventually it was my moment to perform. I was led along the carpet-tiled corridor of the English Department towards a small office. Outside the window, a line of large leafy trees waved back and forth.

I had boned up on the interviewers before the interview. They were also writers I had never heard of. Though their credentials looked good on the back of their books.

'We've got several interviews today, so we are going to do this on a timer. Once the timer ends that will be the end of the interview,' Michele Roberts told me.*

Patricia Duncker held the timer.

I nodded. 'Okay.'

The interview was brisk and to the point.

'What writers do you admire?' Michele asked.

I launched into what I had liked about their work, desperate to prove I'd done my research.

'That's nice you're read our novels,' Michele cut me off. 'But which books do you really admire?'

Time to accelerate.

'*Cat's Eye* by Margaret Atwood, *The Diviners* by Margaret Laurence, *Oranges are Not the Only Fruit* by Jeanette Winterson.'

Patricia asked, 'Do you see yourself as a New Zealand writer?'

'Yes.'

I elaborated on the virtues of New Zealand. I quoted Janet Frame: 'An underwater moon, dim and secret.'

More questions, more answers.

The line of waving trees outside the office window reminded me of an anecdote about Nabokov.

One day a student told Nabokov, 'I want to be a writer.' Nabokov pointed to a tree outside his office window.

'What kind of tree is that?' he asked the student.

'I don't know,' said the student.

'Then you'll never be a writer,' Nabokov replied.

---

* Michele Roberts also had one of the best pieces of advice for me as an amateur writer: 'Play with your shit.'

Neither Patricia or Michele asked me to name the species of tree outside the office window.

On Day 23 of NaNoWriMo it seemed imperative that I establish exactly what kind of trees are outside the property that doubled as Montag and Linda's house in Truffaut's *Fahrenheit 451*. Anything to help my word count.

I ended up on an old britmovie.co.uk forum.

In 2007 Mark O had asked the group for ideas on where Montag and Linda's ultra-modern looking bungalow was located.

Someone called Christoph404 had suggested looking around the Alton Estate in Roehampton.

Then, another contributor called Dan had cruised Edgecombe Park. He thought he spotted the bungalow, or or at least one that looked similar.

The website was full of men searching for the location of the house.

It turned out that 'Phil' was the one in the know. The bungalow scenes surrounded by silver birches were shot near his house at Edgecombe Park, Crowthorne, Berks.

Silver Birch trees. I had found my answer quickly. The same could not be said for the contributor 'Steve', who wanted the exact address. 'Even just the road name would help a lot.'

The conversation thread was now years out of date so there was no point in telling Steve that the property – a Renway Type

60 bungalow on Linkway, Edgecumbe Park – had been privately sold by Bungalow Industries, a company run by a design duo with a passion for midcentury modernism. Bungalow Industries had been based in the Fahrenheit bungalow until they sold it – and had even made a jazzy online catalogue, featuring photos of the house interior from the movie and this quote from *New Homes Magazine* in 1967:

> How often do we see and hear it advertised? "Houses for modern living" "Houses of advanced design" "Your home for the future" – and yet when a house of sufficiently advanced design was required for *Fahrenheit 451* – set some fifty years ahead in time – the design chosen was a Renway home at Edgecumbe Park, Crowthorne. On this development part of this excellent film was shot, and the residents enjoyed the excitement of seeing Julie Christie, Oskar Werner and producer Francois Truffaut on their very doorsteps.

I bet they did.

A motley crew of Borders staff assembled on the doorstep of the Holiday Inn in East Anglia. We were in Alan Partridge Country now. The team was prepared for long hours and extra pay. The process involved in opening a new Borders store was known as a 'sort' and was scheduled to take two weeks.

On the first day at the Holiday Inn, I called a number about a flat in Norwich and navigated my way there on foot, using only directions from locals. This strategy never worked in London without an A to Z. But in Norwich, everything came together easily.

Except for Borders. The store was based in the newly designed Chapelfield Mall. The build was behind schedule. The staff attended a health and safety session run by the building contractors. We had to wear orange high vis safety vests and hard hats on site. All the new shops struggled to get their products up from the shopping centre basement, sharing two dusty overused elevators. The new general manager was ex-HMV staff. Nickname: Noddy. Noddy had a hot wife. James Blunt's *Beautiful* lit up his mobile every time she called.

I began to joke that Chapelfield was built on an Indian burial ground. This was not entirely unreasonable as the mall was situated next to Saint Stephen's Church and a small cemetery. A cobbled path cut through the cemetery on the Church grounds to the mall. Shoppers had to pass crumbling headstones on their journey towards Chapelfield's new food court, where they could sample the delights of The Pasty Shop, KFC and McDonalds. The dead at rest amongst the lawlessness of the living.

On the first day of the sort we drove past the crumbling walls of the city.

'The wall is medieval,' the manager pointed out, with pride. 'The bricks are made of flint.'

I looked at the missing bricks in the wall. 'When are they going to finish it?' I asked.

1985. The waif in my childhood story checked the clock above the station platform. The man standing next to her cracked his paper, reshuffled the pages and stifled a cough. The child shivered, the wind sliced through the holes in her knitted...

I looked up from my exercise book and sighed. It was the school holidays and I was staying at Dad's house by the sea.

'Bored?' he asked.

I shook my head. The book lay open on the table in front of me. At the top of the page I'd written the title in flowing fancy handwriting: The Forgotten Child. Then I had spent the afternoon drawing the forgotten child. It seemed important to capture what she looked like. Her wispy hair floated to one side, teased away from her face by the wind. A lonely tear dripped from her eye. She waited at the train station. Penniless.

Dad put his book down and stoked the fire. The log in the fireplace slipped a notch, sending a shiver of violent red sparks rushing towards the chimney and out onto the hearth. The cat half opened its eyes. A furry gargoyle poised on the arm of the couch. The cat was Dad's full-time companion, as inscrutable as his books.

'If you had to choose between me and the cat who would you choose?' I asked.

'Why would I have to choose?'

'What if we were in a boat stranded at sea and it was sinking and you had to throw one of us overboard in order to survive.'

'Well,' Dad was reading a book. He looked up from it, paused to sip his tea. 'I would keep Tiger on the boat for as long as possible and hope that we would all be rescued.'

Outside the window, sand tumbled along the driveway. The cat blinked.

I turned back to my story. The forgotten child tapped the arm of the aloof gentleman, standing on the platform. 'Please sir, do you have any change?'

The man turned and looked at the waif. Poor desolate creature. What chance did she have of a good meal let alone a good read?

He fished in his coat pocket. 'How far are you going? How many stages?'

The waif shook her head. Either she was speechless or she just didn't know.

He passed her enough for one stage.

'Thank you, sir,' the forgotten child curtseyed.

Mice danced over the tracks. The mice were as large as erasers; their smoky backs reminded the forgotten child of smudged pencil work. She wondered what it would be like to have whiskers and a tail.

The digital sign above the station flashed mint green: two mins.

Two yellow eyes flared in the blackness of the tunnel. The warm breath of the train blew Allen Lane's newspaper from his hands. The newspaper scuttled along the tiles, arachnid, alive. The headlines on the front page changed, time lurched forward with the train. Commuters huddled closer to the platform's edge. The newspaper flew past, and the mice disappeared, replaced by carriages. People bundled behind glass like upset fish in tanks. The waif in my story grew up.

On the train, she watched the platform slow: 'Manningtree.'

From a nearby seat a woman's seashells mumbled in the snug of her ears.

'MIND THE GAP,' the electronic voice said.

The doors parted. 'Next station: Diss.' The train grit its teeth. Each stop was another opportunity to deposit and collect cash. The forgotten child folded herself into a corner seat and opened her book. 'Denham's Dentifrice…' She passed her tongue over her own teeth: a dream of missing teeth is a dream about money.

At Borders Norwich I learned there were two things customers were interested in: Slow Cooking and Keeping Pet Chickens.

Borders Norwich bestsellers:

1. *Easy Slow Cooker Cookbook*
2. *Extrordinary Chickens*
3. *Don'ts for Wives*

'You must miss your husband,' a new girlfriend said.

'Yes.' On Wednesdays and Thursdays, I ate a sausage roll from Bugdens on route to university. In the evenings I lay on the couch in a pair of pink pyjamas eating Ben and Jerry's and watching *America's Next Top Model*. The show was fronted by supermodel Tyra Banks, a hardened extrovert, who possessed an Amazonian physique and the metallic stare of a maniac. Thank God she wasn't teaching at UEA.

Each week Tyra put the fledging models on the show through a series of exercises. The makeover was always entertaining. Most of the girls in the model house were still teenagers and when their long hair was cut short they cried. I understood. Each Tuesday our masters group met for a three hour crit session. Three students circulated their work a week in advance and the class gave critical feedback, led by the tutor.

'Why does your lead character hate men so much?' my tutor asked.

'Tyra Mail!' The girls in the model house galloped towards the waiting envelope to receive their next challenge.

At the end of each episode the models were summoned before a panel of industry experts. Tyra called each girl forward individually and the photo of the week was bestowed upon one radiant face. 'Congratulations you are still in the running to become America's Next Top Model.'

One by one the girls stepped forward.

Until finally, 'I have two beautiful girls standing before me, but I only have one photograph in my hand.' Tyra's eyes were very blue and penetrating, 'And this photo represents the girl still in the running to become *America's Next Top Model*.' The pair held hands, heads bowed. The clock ticked. Finally, the photograph was revealed.

Tyra gave the loser a chaste cuddle. The loser was then embraced by her fellow models. Sad music serenaded her exit. The camera focused on the girl as she sat on the floor of the model house packing her suitcase, then a long shot of her reflection through the window of the passenger seat, city lights blushing over the young face no longer in the running to become *America's Next Top Model*.

I had no idea my lead character hated men.

In the second semester a group of agents took the two hour train journey from London Liverpool Street to Norwich. The agents were a panel of industry experts. They answered our polite questions about publishing. None of the students asked about money; one of the tutors did. I had never heard of the uber-agent Jonny Geller but at the drinks afterwards he was surrounded by a throng of students, their novels rehearsed into tantalising soundbites and passed out like h'orderves. I loitered near the crisps wearing a white pashmina. I wanted to make a good impression, but the sausage roll diet didn't make for dazzling repartee.

I glanced at Geller across the room. He was A-list all the way.

A female agent from Curtis Brown got drunk on the free wine and asked, 'Why isn't anyone writing like Daphne du Maurier any more?'

I had recently read *Rebecca* for the first time and could empathise. 'Yes, why?' I helped myself to another crisp. 'It's such a great read.' The problem for me was quite simple: I rented a room in a grim semi-detached near a greasy spoon. I had never been to Manderley and chances are I wouldn't be going there anytime soon.

In Bradbury's novel Professor Faber, a retired English teacher, describes books as containing pores; his speech helps to fan the flames of Montag's literary awakening. I had paid little attention to Faber in the book, probably for purely sexist reasons. He's an old man. However, his metaphor about books containing pores was spot on. Everyone wants to write a novel that breaks out.

I did too. But while I was working at Borders Norwich I was too busy writing *Megan loves Merchandising*, a guide to creating in-store displays. The guide was an elastic use of my time and my art school training. It included pictures of a colour wheel and diagrams of book displays (the books represented by squares and rectangles) in an attempt to teach staff the importance of shape, balance and symmetry. I used an image of Magritte's deeply unsexy reverse mermaid *The Collective Invention* to illustrate the importance of surprise and Andy Warhol's infamous Campbell soup cans to show the power of repetition. Stack 'em high, watch 'em fly.

But the essence of my merchandising guide was summarised in the principle of the 'lure book'. The lure book is like a beautiful woman. It can be added to the apex of any display and customers will pick it up. The lure book often (but not always) features a beautiful woman on the cover. While I was at Borders Norwich Dita Von Teese's *Burlesque and the Art of the Teese* was my go-to lure book. The customer won't necessarily buy the lure book but it will draw them into the orbit of a display, making an incidental purchase more likely.

One night at Borders Norwich as I added Dita to a prominent display table I got into a conversation with one of the new Christmas temps, Nate.

'Why are there no good looking women authors,' Nate asked. His body, like his attitude, was buff.

'What about Jordan?' I said.

Glamour model Jordan was big business at the time. So was her alter ego Katie Price. Price was the author of several bestselling autobiographies and novels. I hadn't read any of her books but I enjoyed accessorising her tanned pink hardbacks with a flashy feather boa from Ann Summers.

'Jordan's not a real author,' Nate flexed his wit.

'Okay, what about Zadie Smith?' I said.

Case closed. There was a reason Zadie's author photograph was always on her books and it wasn't because she was a genius.

'She's good looking in a geography teacher kind of way,' Nate conceded.

Maybe he had a point? I'd never merchandised Zadie's back catalogue with a feather boa.

Don't judge a book by its cover, we say, but that's easier said than done. Especially when you're a sales manager. And what about all the great book covers and the great illustrators and designers behind them? Bradbury's *Fahrenheit 451* has inspired Ralph Steadman's fiery eye and blazing pen. I was also impressed by Elizabeth Perez's minimalist concept design for another cover. 'I wanted to spread the book-burning message to the book itself,' she said. 'The book's spine is screen-printed with a matchbook striking paper surface, so the book itself can be burned.' On Perez's white cover the 1 in 451 is a match the reader can remove and use to ignite the spine. Perez's design went viral. Her website was bombarded with hits, her inbox with emails. Perez shares a link to the one inflammatory email she recieved about her design on her blog. 'Did you actually ever read the book?' the anonymous emailer asked. 'Shame on you!'

Day 24 and my rewrite of *Fahrenheit 451* was careening out of control. Word count: 20,721. In my rush to complete NaNoWriMo I'd started describing the mechanical hound as a cross between a Kindle and a Penguin Donkey. The original Penguin Donkey was commissioned by the publisher Penguin and made by an Austrian architect – Egon Riss. In 1939 Riss designed the Penguin Donkey as a portable bookshelf to hold Penguin paperbacks (which had only hit the market four years earlier). The Penguin Donkey is now a modernist classic. I saw one saw in an antique shop on Elm Hill in Norwich. Alas, its price was way out of reach.

The mechanical hound in my redraft was as a repository of information just like the Penguin Donkey, except the hound wasn't made out of bent plywood. He was a bit more high tech and I'd given him an extension cord for a tail too – a nifty detail I stole from a fan's online sketch. Meanwhile, Mildred aka Linda aka Julie Christie had left Montag and gone to work as a sex slave for Ogle, the largest search engine in the world. And in my book, I'd brought Clarisse back to life. She rode the subway to Knolls View dressed as a fireman, and visited Professor Faber at his house instead of Montag. Her manuscript was velcroed inside her fire retardant suit. Her story was all she had!

I had furnished Professor Faber with a mechanical cat. Who was also called Faber. Faber and Faber – get it? But the mechanical cat didn't come with a needle that injected procaine into its victims. Instead, when you pushed its ears and it piped out hot espresso.

The cat sniffed Clarisse's manuscript. And spoke.

'Is it shit?'

Together, Faber and Faber gave Clarisse a quick précis of the merit of her manuscript as the train rushed overhead outside.

Faber passed her a small tin box.

'What is it?' she asked.

'A tinderbox.'

He explained that the tinderbox was a piece of pre-industrial technology that was superseded by the rise of white phosphorus matches, first made in factories by little match girls.

I had gotten the details about the tinderbox from Wikipedia:

'In a book published in 1881 the author predicted that the tinderbox would remain common in households despite the advent of matches or Lucifers as they were then known.'

That poor author. By the time their words were in print the tinderbox was already an antique. Strike one: you're out.

I watched some low-rent Ray Mears on YouTube demonstrate how to ignite a real tinderbox. It looked like hard work. No wonder it was obsolete. It occured to me for the first time that the little match girl in Andersen's story was actually a minimum wage employee.

In my rewrite of F451 books weren't burned, they were outmoded. And the mechanical hound was just another item of merchandise. A gimmick.

Now all I needed was a character to represent Jeff Bezos.

Enter: Iggle Piggle.

I was a supervisor at Borders Norwich when *The Night Garden* became big on TV. The programme was catnip for toddlers and quickly spawned a range of associated merchandise. Shipments of the show's characters Iggle Piggle, Upsy Daisy and Maka Paka arrived on pallets. The stock was received through the swing doors at the back of the mall. Dale and Ade, the two middle aged men who worked in inventory, broke the pallets down in the sort room and arranged the stock onto trollies to be wheeled out on to the shop floor.

Iggle Piggle had a soft blue head shaped like a kidney bean. He had squishy tubes for arms, a bell in his left foot, a squeaker in his tummy, and a rattle in his left hand. Iggle was a dreamer; apparently he left the end of each episode in a boat, for which his red blanket doubled as a sail. I couldn't vouch for that as I had never watched the show.

Maka Paka – small beige and round – was clearly an idiot. And Upsy Daisy looked like a Rastafarian.

The day Iggle arrived I decided to pimp out an omni in his honour.

An omni was a freestanding fixture on wheels. Why omni? I guess because it was an omnivorous display device. My art school degree reached the zenith of its expression in omni design. I smooshed together some blue crepe paper and arranged waves across the top shelf. Iggle set out to sea in a cardboard boat.

The general manager walked past during the boat-making phase. Nicky was benevolent and well read: he could select a book to appeal to any staff member. (For me he recommended George Saunders *The Brief And Frightening Reign of Phil*.) His eyes narrowed as I taped together the cardboard prow. Later he confessed, 'I did wonder how long you were going to spend on that omni.'

Four hours. We outsold every other Borders UK store for *In the Night Garden* products. The toddlers wheeled around the shop recognised the characters and shouted out their names. I noticed that the children did not hold Upsy Daisy in low esteem. *In the Night Garden* was produced by the same team behind the *Teletubbies*. They knew what they were doing.

The guy who played Iggle Piggle was an employee too. Inside that giant blue bean headed suit was a man named Nick Chee Ping Kellington. Where was Kellington now? Probably dressed in some other furry suit, cartwheeling across the screen in a set of make believe.

I spent the rest of Day 24 searching for the monorail extras in the cast list of *Fahrenheit 451* on IMBD.

The only cast member listed was 'Man on carriage.'

What about 'Woman who furtively strokes fox fur draped over her shoulder on carriage'?

And 'Girl who kisses own reflection in window on carriage'?

Their performances had made a much deeper impression on me. Truffaut's monorail scenes supposedly depicted a narcissistic society. Without books to light up their minds, each character had turned inward, towards their own reflection. I looked rather more charitably on the girl who kissed her own reflection in the carriage window. To me her kiss wasn't necessarily aimed at herself, it was probably a practise run – just like that test track outside Chateauneuf, south of Paris.

The interior scenes on the monorail had been bluescreened. The actors and extras were first filmed against a blue background. Then the editor, Thom Noble, dropped the view outside the monorail window into the final footage. Once upon a time, bluescreen was state of the art technology. Nowadays, it's another antique. For me the clunky work of that primitive edit suite was as charmingly vintage as Julie Christie's wardrobe and their modernist bungalow in the suburbs.

In *The Making of F451* Noble explained that Truffaut had intentionally scrambled the technology in the film. The sets included old telephones that were already obsolete in 1966. When Linda gave Montag a manual razor at the breakfast table she told him brightly, 'It's the latest thing!'

Noble had also highlighted Truffaut's snazzy use of optical effects. In *Fahrenheit 451* he used a range of linear wipes that interrupt the illusion of the story, drawing attention to the film as a screen. At the fire station black circles closed in around mugshots of the back of Oskar Werner's head. An auteur's tic or a profound cinematic intervention?

In another key scene the firemen arrived at a children's playground and began to frisk the people in the park for paperbacks. A baby with a miniature book was gently chastised by Cyril Cusak, suited and booted, in his role as Captain Beatty. Cusak waggled his finger back and forth at the baby: Tsk. Tsk. Suddenly, Montag stopped a middle-aged man in an overcoat. Game on.

A black wipe flashed across the screen like a curtain closing over the action. The music struck a solemn note. Go Herrmann!

'That's pure Truffaut!' Noble said. 'I've never seen that in a film before and I've never seen it again.'

The blackness was the sweeping eye of the censor, the cinder on the hearth, a pocket turned inside out. *Clunk.*

In the basement of the LA library Bradbury

dropped another dime into the timer.

At the end of Truffaut's *Fahrenheit 451* busy flurries of snow fell down and coated the book people as they walked back and forth, reading the tomes they were committing to memory. The snow was just a lucky coincidence. April 14th. The last day of filming and it was Julie Christie's birthday.

'Bon Anniversaire, Julie!'

'Ca va?'

'Ca va bien!'

Bradbury once likened plot to the footprints your characters leave in the snow after they've run away to incredible destinations.

But maybe, like me, he was just remembering Truffaut's movie?

At the end of the university year, I put on my Nike Moon boots and waded to Borders Norwich through the snow. The tracks of my moon boots mingled with the soles of other people's shoes.

They may have been on their way to incredible destinations, but chances were, like me, many of them were simply going to work. I walked like an astronaut, my breath fogging the air.

Mickey arrived for the weekend and I picked him up from the train station. We lay in the grim light of my rented bedroom. The mouldy old depressing stuff was upon us.

'Let's have sex,' I said.

'I don't want to,' Mickey replied.

My stomached clenched.

'Then maybe we should split up,' I said.

Unclench.

Divorce was an exciting plot development. We got up and walked the cobbled streets of Norwich. The day was nondescript. Feelings filled the space between us like static. We watched two movies back to back. In Bradbury's novel Montag can't remember where he met Mildred, and she doesn't seem to care. I couldn't remember exactly where I met Mickey either. Like Mildred I was self-interested, absorbed in my own private Idaho, the TVs orbit.

We sat down in a café. My tears came down involuntarily. I was dimly aware of a shaven-headed man sitting at a table in the background. The sole witness to the end of our visa marriage, our five-year relationship.

I wiped my tears away and pulled the sugar bowl towards me.

'You've been my family to me here,' I told Mickey.

It was true. I looked at his face, hungry for its familiarity.

'Years from now, if I get the call that something has happened to you, I'll still be floored,' I said.

'Same here, honey.'

'Are you going to move back to New Zealand?' he asked.

'No.'

The shaven-headed man in the background was still alone. Single?

I played with the sugar in the bowl. Scooping it out, letting it fall from the teaspoon.

'What if you become a really famous actor and end up going out with Angelina Jolie?'

Mickey laughed. 'The same thing could happen with you and your book.'

'I don't want to leave here, then regret not having said everything I wanted to say.'

The shaven-headed man in the background blurred.

I pushed the sugar away.

FIN: the credits rolled up and off screen.

In the evening, I sat in the lounge, drinking red.

Truffaut's film had lain waste to me again. Either that or the wine. Both were deep and penetrating. Depression seemed like an intrinsic part of the bouquet, one of the acquired tastes of adulthood.

What was my word count? Again, I was off track. I thought about Montag's flight from the city, pursued by the firemen after burning down his own house. A row of doors opened on a modernist estate in Roehampton. His death became a staged event on TV.

Oskar Werner hid in a boat at the water's edge. Then a close up: a man's fingers reached out and pulled across the tarpaulin. The firemen buzzed past overhead like fireflies, powered by turbo packs that looked like green fire extinguishers. Apparently, Truffaut was so pissed off with Werner by this stage that he got the extra with the most nicotine stained fingers to act as his hand double.

Take that, Oskar. Werner had ruined all the continuity shots by turning up for the final scene of the film with a new haircut.

The word Fin appearing on screen was also deeply significant. The opening credits to F451 were spoken over a montage of TV aerials; no words appeared on screen until the very end. Progress at last?

The snow struck me as equally metaphoric. Each flake drifted down like a comma or a full stop. The end of someone else's sentence.

Film editor Thom Noble said he found the scene of the book people at the finale of the film a bit cringey and pretentious. He was right. In their tattered rags the book people recited the classics like children learning by rote. A bunch of extras introduced themselves to Montag as books. Tweedledee and Tweedledum were *Alice in Wonderland* volumes one and two. A gingernut appeared as Bradbury's *The Martian Chronicles*. And Montag chose Edgar Allen Poe's *Tales of Mystery and Imagination* to learn by heart. But what about the women authors?

Where was *The Mill on the Floss*?

To the Lighthouse?

Orlando?

Bradbury didn't quote any famous female authors in *Fahrenheit 451*. And even Truffaut had focused on male authors. In one scene Oskar Werner stayed up late reading Dickens by the white glare of the TV.

If the film was remade now they'd at least have to include Harry Potter.

The timer went off.

The White Clown

Lights flicked on and shops stayed open late throughout Chapelfield Mall to cash in on the crowds for the latest Harry Potter book launch.

'You know that footage of the Beatles getting off a plane and there are thousands of people screaming?' our general manager told *The Guardian*. 'Well. It's going to be like that later. But worse.'

Borders Norwich was open until midnight: the witching hour when *Harry Potter and the Deathly Hallows* would be released from strict embargo. The tills were ready for fistfuls of cash, the books had been stacked on trollies in the sortroom like a fleet of mail delivery owls, ready to carry J.K. Rowling's letters into the hands of transported readers. The fate of Harry, Hermonie and Ron would at last be known. I assumed Voldemort would be overthrown.

The queue slithered around the store from late afternoon. Families tossed gnomes in the aisles. The crowd was pumped up on cauldrons of Bertie Botts Every Flavour Beans. Outside Chapelfield Mall, dementors on stilts terrified the queue. A 3-year-old won the fancy dress costume then ran amongst the dementors yelling 'Expecto patronum!'

The spell had worked, at least for J.K. Rowling. Amazon had 2.2m orders and Bloomsbury was releasing the book in ninety-three countries. The final Harry Potter story was a global book-selling occasion. Borders UK had been preparing for weeks. A holiday blackout had been issued. The team on the night shift were as excited as the customers. Bob from the children's section had dressed up as the boy wizard, Potter's lightening bolt scar etched across his forehead in eyeliner. (Glasses: his own.) Our operations manager Eva donned her old school uniform and swanned about as a sexy Hermione. Nicky Boardman, our general manager, was well-suited to his role as captain of the Griffindor Quidditch team. Nicky was benevolent and funny, a good manager. A character you could believe in.

A generic black hat sat on my head like a turret. My cape trailed behind me like a sarcastic comment. 'I'm a miscellaneous witch,' I told Nicky.

Finally, the clock struck midnight. The staff wheeled out the trollies. The crowd squealed. The scanners beeped. The tills rang. I flicked straight to the end; I read about the happy marriages of Harry and Ginny, Ron and Hermione. I tried and failed to suspend my disbelief. My degree was over. So was my marriage.

I had nothing against J.K. Rowling's success. I just wished that a novel would come to me with the same crystalline purity that Harry Potter came to J.K. Rowling. She had a vision of Harry as she sat on a crowded train delayed for four hours between Manchester and London. She looked up and saw his scar. Ideas for a seven book series began to swarm in her head. Rowling didn't even have a pen on her.

In *Fahrenheit 451*, Ray Bradbury imagined a future where books were burned, not mass marketed and turned into multi-million dollar films and merchandise. Bradbury wrote 'The Fireman' in 1950 and completed the final draft of *Fahrenheit 451* in 1953, during the second red scare of the McCarthy era. His uncle was a fireman. His distant ancestor Mary Perkins Bradbury was tried, convicted and sentenced to hang as a witch in Salem in 1692. Her alleged crimes included assuming animal forms, notably a blue boar.

'The Fireman' was originally published by Hugh Hefner in *Playboy*.

SparkNotes said that Bradbury was sensitive to attempts to restrict his free speech and that he had objected to letters he'd received suggesting that he revise his treatment of female or black characters. He saw these interventions as the first step on the road to book burning.

SparkNotes weren't kidding. I've never burned a book literally, but I was about to find out exactly how sensitive the Bradbury estate could be about his intellectual property. In *Fahrenheit 451* Bradbury portrays Mildred as shallow because she watches Reality TV. This seems like another reductive form of censorship to me. Shallowness is not prized as a redeeming quality. Hence the snobbery around popular fiction and romance novels. This is a snobbery I have often been part of – e.g., I have never read Jodi Picoult but I have not let that stand in the way of judging her. Jodi writes books the way other people bake muffins. There's always a new batch on the way. Still, she also has the best advice for writers. You can't edit an empty page.

The timer went off.

Day 25: I woke up and set the timer on my iPhone. Monday. Only five days left to nail NaNoWriMo. I sat at my desk and made a list of topics that still needed to be addressed:

- *The White Clown* – significance of?
- The Sea of Faith.
- The end of the world – but make it funny.
- Amazon opening a physical bookstore but make it...

I was approaching the novel as though it was work. Trying to squeeze out a chapter felt like trying to lose five kgs. Technically it was possible to lose a kg a week. Tehnically it was possible to write a chapter a week. Maybe even two. If I went to the gym I usually felt better about myself afterwards. If I wrote I usually felt better about myself too. It was just a matter of showing up.

But I was showing up. That was the problem. I'd turned Mildred into a pale – better looking – fascimile of myself. That wasn't fair on her or Julie Christie. Let alone Ray Bradbury. I wasn't honouring his authorial intentions. Instead I was revealing my achilles heel. One of the first things many great fiction writers seem keen to point out is that they are not writing about themselves. Eleanor Catton won the Booker Prize in 2013 and in one of her interviews she said she plans to never write a book about someone writing a book. I felt a shiver of self-revulsion. To write about yourself is to be self-interested. The 'I' is often equated with triviality.

Reality TV is also abhorred for its pettiness. Like many liberal people I instantly hated the idea of *Big Brother*, then found myself able to watch loads of it. Even readers with the vaguest literary affilations to George Orwell were sure he would despise 1984 being coopted in such a commercial, morally reprehensible way. 'Poor Orwell must be turning in his grave,' we said. Yet millions participated in the weekly votes for Big Brother UK selecting the candidate they wanted evicted by phone or text message. I hated the concept of Reality TV because I objected to cheap banality. But in the end it was the cheap banality that most captivated me. I liked watching the Big Brother contestants sitting on the couch doing nothing as the digitial clock appeared in the corner of the screen and a disembodied voice intoned the day and the hour. In night vision the contestant's sheets wriggled with anonymous limbs, their eyes blinked, mint green.

My own threshold for Reality TV was high. So who was I to judge? When ex-Big Brother contestant Jade Goody was diagnosed with cancer I thought it was a marketing stunt. Sometimes it's hard not to read illness as a metaphor. Goody was diagnosed with cervical cancer a year after bullying the Bollywood star Shilpa Shetty in the *Celebrity Five Big Brother* House. Goody referred to the actress as 'Shilpa Poppadom'. At the time Goody was supporting an anti-bullying charity, her first autobiography was on the market, as well as her first perfume, *Shh*. By the time

Goody was voted out of Celebrity Big Brother in 2007, Channel 4 had recieved 54,000 complaints about the bullying. I couldn't help but feel sorry for Goody. She was originally prized for her ignorance. She thought Rio de Janeiro was a person and Norwich was in East Angula. Goody was given the diagnosis of her cancer in the diary room of the Indian Big Brother *Bigg Boss*. She died on 22 March 2009. Her funeral was of course broadcast live on Sky News, but her death also helped raise awareness of cervical cancer amongst a demographic the NHS struggles to reach – the young and the less well-educated.

'Focus on the list,' my inner critic said.

'Tick the bullet points off one by one.'

The whiteface is the oldest of the clown archetypes. When whitefaces perform with other clowns, they usually function as the straight man, 'top banana' or the leader of the group.

I had been putting off tackling *The White Clown* in *Fahrenheit 451*, partly because Bradbury hadn't give me much to go on. All I knew was that Mildred's favourite TV show featured clowns chopping each other's limbs off to the sound of what I presumed was canned laughter. Was it a metaphor for Reality TV? I hoped so. Because I didn't want to respond to *The White Clown* literally. Half the enjoyment of reading literature was collecting the symbols like charms on a bracelet then holding them up to the light. Even SparkNotes didn't seem to have a point of view on *The White Clown*.

In Bradbury's book Mildred was ecstatic when her friends come over to watch her favourite show. But her husband spoilt it by reading poetry. To be fair, having your favourite TV series interrupted is annoying. Even when the poem's as good as Matthew Arnold's 'Dover Beach'. Poor Arnold wrote 'Dover Beach' in the late nineteenth century, never knowing that it would be used to bore Mildred shitless in the twentieth cenutry. The scene marked a turning point in the novel. Mildred can't ignore Montag's flagrant disregard of the law anymore. He's not only smuggling books into their house and hiding them. He's also reading them. Aloud! To her! And her friends!

Bradbury depicted Mildred and her friends in *Fahrenheit 451* as stooges, punctuated by exclamation marks. Their general knowledge was as rubbish as Jade Goody's. Their moral crimes included elective c-sections and getting over husbands who died in wars. They didn't like children. They were selfish. Vain. Self-serving. The wives were owners of condos on the river denial. In hindsight, it didn't seem like such a bad place to own a property.

I tried to rewrite the scene from Mildred's perspective.

In my draft Mrs Phelps and Mrs Bowles arrive early to watch *The White Clown*. They play cards together, do lines of coke and drink white wine and then red wine when the white wine runs out.

'How long do we have?' one asks.

'Long enough for me to finish this line.'

Outside, the moon was only a sliver away from full. A metaphor leapt onto the tip of my tongue. I felt it tap-tap-tapping, but it wouldn't come.

I got Mildred up from her chair to pour a Martini – a sly reference to Bradbury's wife Maggie, who was allegedly partial to one or two.

A disembodied voice intoned, 'Day 21, 9pm.'

The cameras rolled. The theme song to *The White Clown* began. I dressed Mrs Bowles as a harlequin. No one would be able to tell by the litheness of her checkered leotard that she'd had two children at all. Mrs Phelps was a hobo, she toyed with the ratty buttons on her dead husband's military jacket, pressed a button and water shot out of the plastic flower on the lapel. And Mildred was the white clown; she sat immobile in her silk outfit and said nothing at all.

Bradbury had many talents but dialogue wasn't one of them. If I opened Mildred's mouth she had to say the words he had written for her – and that was a problem, because the Mildred in my head just didn't sound that stupid.

A symbol crashed.

I turned back to Truffaut's film to see how the auteur had handled the same material. Julie Christie looked especially superb in this scene. I loved the creaminess of her long silken dress, cinched at the waist, so fluid to watch. Christie's on-screen prescene was as luminous as the dress. Surely, its pale-ness was no accident? The dress was a slice of the moon in all its loveliness, its swoon. At one point in this scene Christie reaches up and touches her bangs. (She bangs, she bangs.) Her blonde hair – every bit as redolent as Nabokov's *Pale Fire* and much quicker to read.

The costume designer on the set of *Fahrenheit 451* was Tony Walton. Clearly the man was a genius. He was married to Julie Andrews, his childhood sweetheart, when he worked on F451. He fell in love with Andrews after watching her play an egg in a stage production of Humpty Dumpty. I loved that he wanted to hump Humpty. It was about the sweetest thing I'd ever heard.

In Truffaut's F451 Tony's choice of costume metaphorically associated Christie with the white clown. I like to think that's because Walton understood Humpty's peril, knew what it was to play the egg. I thought of Pierrot, the white clown, who graced so many little girls bedrooms in the 1980s with that sweet sentimental stare, pierced by one agile tear. I had once owned a Pierrot beachtowel. I freaking loved that towel. What had happened to it?

I still loved Pierrot. The way I still loved the moon. I wanted to write about such things without shame or further adieu, the way Bradbury had gorged on his own metaphors. He claimed he had no idea what the word metaphor even meant when he wrote *Fahrenheit 451*. I loved reading him even when his imagery seemed too inflated, too hopped up on its own helium. At the beginning of *Fahrenheit 451* Clarisse tells Montag to taste the rain. She twirls a dandelion under his chin and talks to him about the man in the moon. But how could she be so sure it was a man up there? What about Pierrot? Her acrobatic legs swung over the waning crescent, her fabulous neck ruff ruffled. Ready to merchandise her heart out.

The sales managers of Borders UK gathered in a small flourscent lit room on the edge of London. It might as well have been

Staines. A motivational speaker who looked like David Brent had been hired to help us think outside the box. 'What if?' he asked. It was the storyteller's weapon. What if we didn't promote the next Dan Brown book? What if we offered customers the chance to trade in their copies of The Da Vinci Code instead? They could choose other *better* books that were not written by Dan Brown. At the time, I was jazzed up on the idea. Radical! What if we stopped selling Jodi Picoult next? The David Brent lookalike encouraged us to dig deep. What did our customers really want?

We thought outside the box then we crossed the street to the local Westfield shopping centre and thought inside it. Our task was to compare field notes on our experiences as customers. Why was Apple so successful? Because it produced outstanding products? No! Because it had geniuses on the shop floor providing customer focused retail experiences.

As we journeyed back to our respective Borders stores, Christmas appeared like a mirage on the horizon.

I made an extra effort to talk to customers.

'What made you choose this title?' I asked the little old lady across from the till from me.

'No one does men like Georgette Heyer.'

'You have to read this,' a male customer told me.

'What is it about that book?' I asked.

'It's her. Lisbeth Salander.' He exited away with a dreamy smile. Clearly, the girl with the dragon tattoo was smoking.

One day as I replenished the large 3-for-2 table in the front of store, a woman held up Kate Atkinson's latest novel: *When Will there Be Good News?*

'How's this doing?' she asked.

'It's one of our bestsellers,' I replied. 'It's been very popular.'

She slapped the book back down on the table.

'Well, I read it from front to back and there wasn't any good news in it.'

The timer went off.

'Amazon is not happening to bookselling, the future is happening to bookselling,' Jeff Bezos told correspondant Charlie Rose on *60 Minutes* in 2013. I agree. But it is easier to make that statement when you're the CEO of Amazon and have set up your own company – Blue Origin – to lower the cost of domestic spaceflight for future generations, so that everyone can afford to explore the solar system.

According to Brad Stone, the author of *The Everything Store: Jeff Bezos and the Age of Amazon*, Bezos dismantled his own crib with a screwdriver when he was three years old. Blimey. The future happens to all of us. Some sleep in cribs. Others lower the cost of space-flight. As the global recession swung into action, I could hear the distant whirr of a screw driver. The final bolts began to fall out of the Borders business model.

Our in-store CD sales plummeted as the music industry adapted not to illegal downloading, Apple and the iPod, but to the future. Ditto, DVD's. Borders last made a profit in 2006.

The original Borders founders Tom and Louis had long since sold out to Kmart, and now the American Mothership was casting off the international arms of its operation. Borders UK was sold to Luke Johnson's Capital Risk Partners in Autumn 2007. Borders Australia, New Zealand and Singapore were sold in 2008 to Pacific Equity Partners, then on to RedGroup Retail.

In the UK stores the Borders uniform was introduced: a short sleeved shirt and a sweatshirt. The colour: fire engine red.

Our stock began to flow. One way. Out the door.

Deliveries stalled.

In 2008 Borders UK dismantled its central warehouse in favour of direct supply to shops from publishers and wholesalers in order to aid efficiency. At the same time, Waterstones – our competition – introduced a centralised warehouse instead of direct supply to shops from publishers and wholesalers in order to aid efficiency.

Nicky relocated to Borders Islington, then on to Apple.

'Don't look at me like that,' he said.

'Like what?' I said.

'Like you want to kill me.'

We relocated humour and installed several bays of beige office stationary on the ground floor. Stationary = high margins.

Fridges gurgled at till points. Borders had branched into bottled water and confectionary. Browsing is thirsty work.

'What will I do if Borders goes under?' I asked the new general manager.

'I don't know, but it's a good question.'

I took a promotion and relocated to Borders Kingston-Upon-Thames – one of the five worst performing stores in the company.

The general manager sat in his windowless office and told me he was leading from the back. True. He was also planning his wedding. A team of booksellers told me everything that was wrong with the store. The staff felt short-changed. I promised change. I was leading from the front. I was also rearranging the sidelines in the till queue.

'This ship is sinking fast,' the unofficial matriarch of the store told me.

I was merchandising a table in the front of store at the time. I may as well have been rearranging the deck chairs on the Titanic.

At Borders head office on Charing Cross Road, I was introduced to the new head of marketing. He proudly showed me the new logo he'd been working on. The strapline featured the image of a butterfly made from the pages of a book. The new catchphrase: *Let's Escape*.

The problem with Borders UK was not our lack of stock or inability to compete on pricing – it was our branding.

The marketing team were leading from the back.

The CEO visited and asked where the extra shelving units had gone. I told him I had removed them in order to tighten up the remaining stock. He told me that the absent units compromised the integrity of the store. Integrity?

In the mornings I gave up-beat team briefings.

'What would motivate you?' I asked.

'Gin,' the matriarch replied.

I set the sales target for the day and promised the team a bottle of gin if they reached it.

At another shift meeting the matriarch looked me over and sneered, 'You're a bit corporate, aren't you?'

My anger erupted into flames. I had paid for the gin from my own pocket.

The basement flooded. Once. Twice. Again. Oil from the resturant next door kept clogging the drains. The staff and I swept water back and forth over the carpet tiles. I cordoned off the basement. It didn't matter. There was no stock in the multi-media fixtures anymore. Just dust. The carpet retained the stink of the drains even after the cleaners had been and gone. The basement smelt fetid. Rank. There was only one thing left to do.

Day 26. On the set of Pinewood studios in 1966, Thom Noble swivelled back and forth in his chair in the cutting room. The clock was ticking. He had to finish the film.

He ran the dailies once more just to watch her performance again.

Extraordinary. She lifted the whole scene. Oskar Werner's reading of the poem was sufficent but it wasn't moving. Ann Bell made it work. And who was she? No one really. A bit part. One of the wife's friends. Noble had spent all afternoon trying to get the cut right. Her face was tentative at first, then as the words took their toll, she began to weep. Not at once. Just softly.

Softly. Her tears as spontaneous as snow, little eddies drifting down. She alone captured the vulnearabilty of the scene, she made the poetry plausible. The powder blue dress she wore on screen just laid an extra claim to her sadness.

Noble had been on set so long. He blinked. His mouth tasted of tea. He closed his eyes. Hours swilled. No one else would ever know her peformance this intimately. Second by second. Frame by frame.

Truffaut knocked on the door.

'C'est merveilleux,' the director agreed. 'Mais trop long.'

The few seconds that remained showed Ann in her blue dress, dabbing at the corners of her eyes. Poetry has affected her cruelly.

'Have-a-g-ood-weekend.' Truffaut smiled and waved.

Noble knew Bell's performance was something special. He hoped her career would bear it out. For now the footage was gone, the magic lost.

He'd learned his first major lesson as editor. By cutting something too much you simply lose it. It falls through the cracks and it's gone.

Day 27. In the public library, I opened my MacBook Air and watched my word count graph spike towards the finish line. Some of the other participants were already there. The clock was ticking. The collective word count sprinting towards victory.

Bradbury said that *Fahrenheit 451* had contained a paradox. My book also contained a paradox. I just didn't know what it was.

Bradbury's narrative arc was crystal clear. After watching *The White Clown*, Mildred dobs Montag into the firemen. Captain Beatty arrives at their house in his jaunty salamander. Montag and Beatty prepare to face off. Freedom of speech must win the day. Mildred clutches her baggage and exits in a beetle-taxi – not knowing that Bradbury plans to kill her off in an atomic bomb blast for the finale.

I followed Bradbury's lead, but I had something extra up my sleeve. Lucky Strikes. Also an upgrade to the driver's seat.

I wrote: *Mildred burned through the streets like a criminal in Grand Theft Auto, a cigarette hung from her lower lip. 80s pop songs sizzled past billboards on the fritz; the rain was programmed to fall and it did. She headed away from nature, into the city – that's where the action was. It was a relief to shuck off the suburbs and all the mouldy old depressing stuff. Let's escape!*

Across my laptop screen she followed a road beside a train track that looped through a forest of automated trees. In Bradbury's *Fahrenheit 451* nature is a sanctuary, a place to hide from the city. But that was just because Bradbury hadn't forseen 3D printing. Nature can be manufactured just like everything else.

I wrote: *The trees along the side of the highway stood still as totem poles. Their leaves and branches embossed the sky. The mechanical forest was modelled in the form of oak and pine trees. The trees had originally worked on timers; set inside each trunk was a cuckoo clock and the leaves had once turned like the hands, indicating the time of day. The forest* had been someone's great idea for the future, but like most great ideas it didn't work. The trees had lost their wiring, the cuckoos in their trunks had sprung their springs and time had unwound. No one came to the mechanical forest to be close to nature.

A bullet train shot over the track. Cuckoo.

I looked up and watched a librarian wheel a trolley of books past. A copy of an old Julie Christie biography sat on the desk beside my MacBook. Research. The book was an old hardback, with a turquoise cover, its laminate coming undone. I had only read the chapter on *Fahrenheit 451*. The train I was writing about could have been on route to the nearest station to Pinewood studios. Cuckoo. Or it could have been a test track like the Chanteneuf south of Paris. Cuckoo. Or it could have even been the antique model train set that Julie Christie gave Truffaut as a gift on the set of *Fahrenheit 451*. Cuckoo.

The librarian turned another aisle and began plugging the books back into their order on the shelf. Time to accelerate:

A flash of ash across the page – Mildred swerved, and the beetle span around 180 degrees. The tyres released the scent of rubber. In the rear vision mirror, a flash of mint green.

The hound lay on its side. She opened the door. One of them was panting. The rain lashed its tail again. She walked towards the hound, her stilettos lit green.

Cipher and machine regarded one another.

It was a touching moment so I wrote: *Mildred held her hand over her heart. Still running.*

The hound scanned the side of the road as though wishing it could run into the safety of the trees. Mildred admired the ingenuity in its manufacturing. Heat rose from its hard drive. She bent down in her pencil skirt and held out her hand.

Warm like a live body. She stroked the mechanical hound. A robotic pet she could rely on. A husband, not so much.

The librarian finished shelving and wheeled the empty trolley away. The wheels squeaked and I remembered other trollies, other books shelved.

A chorus of drones blazed across the night sky. The pair turned and watched.

The proboscis extended from inside the hound's mouth.

On the tip: a reading light switched on, then off.

Word count: 27,418. I closed my laptop. The apple blanked. Just another reading platform.

'There is more than one way to burn a book. And the world is full of people running about with lit matches,' Ray Bradbury said, in the afterword to the 1979 edition of *Fahrenheit 451*.

I know what temperature books burn at. Half price.

On 26 November 2009, I attended a conference call in the office. The senior managers and general managers of the remaining forty-five Borders UK stores were on the other end of the line. The CEO spoke. He told us that despite all our best efforts the chain had been placed into voluntary administration. MCR had been appointed as the company to handle the administration period and were now legally in control of all the chain's assets, including the stores.

The worst was happening.

I put the phone down. I laughed.

Each store was bequeathed a retail consultant, a representative of MCR. Our retail consultant, Gordon, arrived later that day carrying a plastic bag filled with sale signage. The drama. On the evening of the 27th of November 2009, it was announced that a closing down sale would commence in all stores on the following day. In the windows Borders staff erected the sale signs in glaring states of emergency.

Gordon had a potbelly and a robust sense of humour. He was used to resentment; his attitude could best be described as resigned. He told me that I would be surprised by the value this experience would add to my CV.

He was married and emitted a vague aroma of stifled sexual energy. Or perhaps that was me? He told me what to do, and I made the staff do it.

The sale began. More signage arrived.

The queue turned into a conga line of shoppers driven insane by bargains, bays, tables, gondolas strip searched, tills banging open and closed, Lady Gaga caught in a *Bad Romance*. A customer mentioned that the volume was inappropriate. I agreed.

Shoppers offered their condolences. 'So you're all out of jobs? I'm sorry.' Then bought stacks of books for under half price and watched their receipts like Scrooge McDuck. I had a loud argument with a young couple convinced they had been cheated out of 2p. I told them I didn't give a fuck.

The next customer waiting in the queue was children's author Jacqueline Wilson. She was sorry.

The timer went off.

On Day 28 Sooty O'Donahue, the NaNoWriMo character bearing my porn-name, woke up inside a terrible farce. Eyes blinked open. The whiteness of space. Above her head a bank of florescent lights were on the fritz.

She sat up. Concrete walls. Rows of industrial clad blue shelving.

A poster of *Touch Not the Cat*.

A voice over the tannoy said, 'Dear customers, this store will close in ten minutes. If you do have any final purchases you'd like to to make please take them to the staff at the ground floor tills who will be happy to serve you.'

A giant soft toy appeared at her side. He had a blue head shaped like a kidney bean and held a red blanket in his hand.

'Where am I?' Sooty asked.

'The sort room,' Iggle Piggle giggled.

'I think I've lost the plot,' Sooty said.

'It's time to sort it out,' Iggle said.

A door opened and Iggle walked through it, trailing his bed time blanket. Sooty followed. She noticed a few empty trolleys abandoned at one end of the coridor and a fire extinguisher attached to the wall. Above it was a map outlining the staff collection point incase of fire. Cartoon flames gushed from the square that represented Borders.

They passed multiple swing doors. Sooty stopped and looked through a window at a cavernous packing centre, huge blue cranes patrolled the endless aisles and conveyerbelts carried a miscellaney of products past a row of automated assembly workers.

Iggle motioned her forward. He zipped along pretty quickly for a creature who was essentially as big as a dwarf.

They turned another corner. At the end was a large door marked *Management Only*. Sooty pressed her lanyard over the grey button. The door swung open and they both went through. Sooty peered down another corridor that stretched into the distance. 'This place is bigger than I thought.'

A voice over the tannoy announced, 'All aboard the Ninky Nonk.'

A train with a banana for an engine pulled up, Iggle and Sooty stepped into the carriage, the bells and klaxons sounded and off they went.

At the first door along the corridor the Ninky Nonk pulled to a halt. A mechanical hound with eyes as big as teacups guarded the door. But Sooty didn't drink tea. She prefered a Flat White, even if it was from Starbucks.

The hound stood up. 'I am the keeper of the key to the Medieval Library. Inside are many treasures: *The Decamaeron*, *The Canterbury Tales*, *The Consolation of Philsophy*. Including all the sales figures for the era.'

Iggle said, 'Doggie.'

'Would you and your companion care for a reading? Perhaps *Beowulf*?'

Sooty held out her hand. 'Sorry, but I'm on the timer.'

'What about a recital from *The Diseases of Women*?'

As the Ninky Nonk sped off she heard him howling: 'What were we war-danes in our yore days...'

'He needs to get another job,' Mildred said.

Iggle laughed. '*The Book of Job*.'

The mechanical hound at the second door had eyes as large as dinner plates. Not that people neccessairly ate off dinner plates. Sooty often ate off microwave trays because it saved on time, especially when she was on the night shift. Still, she recognised the dinner plate as a cultural artifact.

The mechanical hound wore a white neck ruff and a quill behind one ear.

'To be or not to be, that is the question.' The hound stood on his hind legs, barked and ran around in a circle. His tail wagged.

Shakespeare and Iggle seemed to hit it off. One was a genius who had stood the test of time. The other had a bit further to go.

Shakespeare and Iggle compared their worldwide net worth, but Sooty was too discreet to possibly outline the frontrunner.

They alighted the Ninky Nonk more and sped off along the corridor.

They came to the third door and stepped off.

The mechanical hound from *Fahrenheit 451* stood up on his eight legs. His green eyes glowed. But he didn't have a probiscus because it was too difficult to imagine what a hound with a probiscus would look like.

'Everything's got a bit messy,' Sooty said. 'There are so many different characters and stories colliding in this corridor I don't know how to keep everything straight. I'm just glad that we finally managed to crowbar something from Hans Christian Andersen into the mix again, because frankly the reference to 'The Tinderbox' has really been bothering me. '

'What's behind this door,' Sooty asked. 'Extra margin?'

The mechanical hound stepped aside.

She opened it and discovered the staff toliet.

The hound and Iggle waited outside.

Sooty sat on the toilet and listened to the sound of her own pee.

She sighed, there were so many books in the world. Too many. She reached for the loo paper and discovered the roll was empty. The company account was on stop again.

At her feet sat a pile of old Jodi Picoult novels.

Sooty tore the title page from *My Sister's Keeper*.

The voice over the tannoy said, 'Borders on the verge of collapse.'

'Borders had a whiff of the *Friends* generation about it,' said Bookseller UK's editor-in-chief Neill Denny. 'It was very of its time and all set up to sell cultural stuff like books, CDs and DVDs to hip young things. But the market changed around it – in the end the Friends left New York and moved to suburbs and were in fact the generation that was first to start shopping online.'

I was galled to be implicated as a statistic of the *Friends* generation. Why? I knew Chandler, Monica, Phoebe, Rachel and Ross. I even knew the name of Ross's pet monkey, Marcel. I'd watched *Friends*, but I was not one of them. The show didn't reflect my education, economic situation or lifestyle. I didn't take *Friends* literally.

I worked at Borders because I thought it would help me become a better writer. Just by shelving Dan Brown I'd get better at keeping my reader glued to the page. I read the first pages of novels. I read the last pages. I looked at literary masterpieces as though they were runes that might cast my own fortune. By touching their spines I'd release my inner genius and write a classic in a fever, trancelike – it would be as easy as watching *Friends*. The characters would move through me like ghosts.

In childhood my first stories were about demonic possession. As a teenager I tried science fiction, inspired by the cover art. I wrote about a dragon preparing to fly out of a cave. I didn't know what the dragon would do next. In high school I finished a romance in the style of *Sweet Valley High* and kept it in a mauve ring binder. And in late 2002 *The Borders of Love* evaporated like the froth of a Starbucks cappuccino, before my job was swept away by the flood of online retail and – of course – the future.

At the time Borders UK was unravelling Dad emailed me, 'I'd love to get my hands on the BBC Don Cupitt program broadcast in the 1980s called *Sea of Faith*.'

I ordered him a copy on Amazon.

The sea of faith ebbs in and out.

The title is a reference to a line in Matthew Arnold's poem 'Dover Beach'. The SparkNotes website prompted students to read 'Dover Beach', asking why it was significant that Montag reads this poem to Mildred and her friends in *Fahrenheit 451*? Good question. I imagined the poem might just be something Brabury pulled from the shelves at the UCLA library. He probably shut his eyes, opened the page and put his finger down. Hey presto!

Personally, I loved Arnold's poem, especially the line about the sea of faith withdrawing. The poem described the withdrawal of religious faith but I had believed in the power of literature and the tide had gone out on that too.

Perhaps, in hindsight, some Virgina Woolf might have struck more of a chord with Mildred and her friends? If Montag had been serious about converting the women to literature he could have tried harder to appeal to their sensibilities. What self-respecting modern woman doesn't require *A Room of One's Own*? I didn't think it was so wrong to add a wall screen – or three – to Woolf's original shopping list. Let's face it, a woman needs something to put in a room of her own – and sometimes after writing it's nice to flick through Netflix. Netflix doesn't have *The Hours* of course, which is a shame because Nicole Kidman looks so intellectual playing Virgina Woolf in that prosthetic nose.

According to IMBD Kidman loved wearing the prosthetic nose and wore it off screen and on. Woolf's nose became an item of camoflauge for Nicole, a pyschic shield that protected her from the paparazzi's damaging rays during her split from Tom Cruise. I knew just what Nicole was thinking as she pushed her feet into a pair of stilettos and exited the set of *The Hours* each day: let's escape.

I opened up my laptop. The first job I saw online was for the general manager of Borders Wellington. It was time to go home.

I arrived only to discover that Borders down under was going under fast.

'Do you have any maps of Wellington?' a customer asked.

'No.'

'Do you realise we're in Wellington?'

'Yes.'

The New Zealand Borders stores were owned by Redgroup Retail, a private company that also owned Angus and Robertson in Australia and Whitcoulls in New Zealand. Whitcoulls is the equivalent of WHSmith, a bookstore drained of all romance by florouscent lighting, children's gifts and games. The word literature doesn't belong shrink wrapped in the aisles amongst the greeting cards. If Ray Bradbury had walked into Whitcoulls he would turned around and walked out, with a Lotto ticket in his back pocket.

In New Zealand the Borders instore café was called Gloria Jeans, another terrible Australian franchise. At least Starbucks was a Moby Dick reference. Gloria Jeans sounded like a character from *Kath and Kim* – one who enjoys a large glass of Khardonnay. The buying for the New Zealand Borders stores had also been centrally managed from the Australian head office. That explained why Borders Wellington had a stack of twenty-five hardbacks on keeping Australian houseplants: the joys of automated allocation.

Still, there were benefits. I read *Monkey Grip* by Helen Garner and *Candy* by Luke Davies. The Aussies do junkie stories so well. The fiction bays were as gap-toothed as an addict's rotting smile. I spent the next few months removing shelving. I checked the dates on the binc stickers of untranslated French and Italian novels. Dead wood. The poetry section in Wellington was skimpier than a g-string. Crime had shrunk to the usual suspects: Dan Brown's latest.

The 2010 Redroup Retail conference was held in a hotel outside Brisbane. The climate was humid. The ideas overripe; the company running a high temperature. A motivational speaker was brought in to do a workshop on positive thinking. The staff were asked to suspend their disbelief. Perhaps branching into gifts and homeware was the answer? A customer could pick up a copy of Jamie Oliver's *Fifteen Minute Meals* and compliment it with Jamie Oliver's cheeky coasters or a 'Big Boy' Barbeque.

I remembered the David Brent lookalike from Borders UK and finally saw him for what he was: *The Lost Symbol*.

In Brisbane the powers that be came up with the same answers to the same problems. RedgroupRetail thought the solutions to the problems of trying to run a large chain bookstore were stationary (high margin) an extended range of gifts and Kobo ereaders. (Elonex: RIP.) Kobo was an important investment in the company's future, we were told. The mechanical hound strained on its leash. The CEO sprang on stage and introduced the concept of the company as a content provider. Not a bookstore.

But the final straw was when the a bubbly blonde from the marketing department got up on her soap box and addressed the conference. She detailed the findings of a recent survey which revealed that Borders staff didn't even like customers. They liked books.

'Is the direction of the company clearer to you now?' my boss asked.

At Borders Wellington I found a small paperback called *The Yellow Lighted Bookshop* mishelved in fiction. The book was the true story of an American bookseller named Lewis Buzbee. Buzbee outlined the cycle of a bookstore so well. By the time the shelves begin to thin out, the store is already in a terminal state of decline. He wrote about how the employees of Silcon Valley, the winners of the dot-com boom, bought their computer books from the book shelves, but were also the first early adopters who migrated to shopping online.

I thought of my own meagre beginnings tending Computers, Maths and Science at Borders Islington. The computers section had a small window that looked out over Sainsburys and a small sidestreet. On the night shift I sometimes stared out into the blackness. I admired the residue of faded stars above Sainsburys. On those long quiet nights I felt as though I was inside a black hole, shelving the cosmos. Light years away, I had slipped into another dimension, neither a writer, a bookseller or a content provider – just a person trying to find order in the strange deep abundance of the galaxy.

I cried as I read *The Yellow Lighted Bookshop*. In the end it's the truth we take to heart.

On 17 February 2011, RedGroup Retail (including the Borders, Angus & Robertson as well as Whitcoulls chains) were placed into voluntary administration. All the Borders Australia stores were closed and the New Zealand stores were rebranded Whitcoulls.

The timer went off.

Day 29 and I was finally closing in on that cool 50,000.

I set the timer: *The war was over in 45 minutes. The drones flew in formation like a v of birds migrating south for winter. People ran through the streets as bombs fell. On multiple floors of gleaming high-rise buildings office workers paused at photocopiers, water coolers gulped, people in apartment blocks looked up from their screens as the grey-beaked drones advanced carrying their cargo of first-world problems.*

The inner shriek of a stomach, a muscle flexed, wincing, running, little time, the sky cracked open, buildings blazing like heads on fire. A second sequence of drones streaked across the sky on a timer. A child hid inside beneath a table, hands clamped over his ears as the wallscreen forecast the end of the world.

Howling. All data lost, only blank screens.

Tangled electricity lines sparked on the streets.

Fires swept through the city unbidden, looking for reasons to burn, latching on to anything, orange tongues lashing.

At the station, the hound blinked. Tried to stand on its haunches. Blackness. The swirl of ash. A mechanical whimper. The hound's hard drive sifted, heat coursing out of its air vent at the back. A shaft of light. The hound blinked again. A chain gang worked from above, passing rubble from the collapsed fire station down into the street. A blonde, her face covered in soot, lifted a brick from the station and yelped. A guttural sound of excitement, of pain.

'It's a dog,' she cried. Across the broken shards of the city, flames danced, turned. Who would put them out?

A fireman walked towards her dressed in his frayed uniform, his face no longer distinguised. It took a minute to recognise him. He must have been caught in the explosion, standing near the heat.

'I am Fahrienhiet 451,' he said.

'I know.' They touched hands. A light drizzle fell on their shoulders. Or perhaps it was just more atomic ash? Either way, she shivered. He wasn't wearing his wedding ring anymore. Nor was she.

'I guess this is the end,' he said.

'Of the world or of our marriage?'

'Of the chapter in the autobiography.'

'Yes,' she agreed. 'Although to be honest I'm not sure I can even write in chapters.'

He let go of her hand.

Neither of them wanted to get into the mouldy old depressing stuff again.

'Hey, what do you think's a better title,' I looked up from my laptop. '*The Borders of Love* or *The White Clown?*'

'*The Borders of Love* sounds a bit Mills and Booney.'

'So, *The White Clown?*'

'I don't like clowns,' my boyfriend said.

It was the end of the line—

The timer went off.

In the spring of 1950 the subway richocheted past Venice Beach, shaking the rented apartment. Up and down, back and forth. Ray Bradbury brushed his teeth. Up and down. Back and forth. One day someone should design a mechanical toothbrush! He could put one in his new story. Or would that be overdoing it? He peered into the bathroom mirror.

'Ray?'

'Mmm?'

'Are you ready for bed?'

Maggie leant against the doorframe in her pale nightdress. The glow of the reading light behind her; the curve of her hips, the outline of her breasts, swollen with milk.

He splashed cold water over his mouth. The toothpaste hung from his chin in a foaming santa beard, down the plughole with a slurp.

'Ready.'

In bed, he put his arm around her. Her hand warm on his chest. He felt fully charged. He could feel the alertness in her body too, that part of her that was now permanently on call for their baby. A watchfulness. He kissed her forehead and turned the reading light off.

'What do you think?' he asked in the darkness.

'It's good,' she said.

'Really?' he knew it was good, felt the urgency of the story; he only had a few dimes left now, he'd finish 'The Fireman' tomorrow. Electric!

'You know it's good,' Maggie laughed.

She stroked her foot along his calf muscle, everything just right.

'What about all the quotes,' he said, 'from other books?'

'I liked them.'

The curtains were drawn but if they had been open it wouldn't have mattered, they had no view to speak of in LA. Just the side of a building. No moon, no stars. It didn't matter, Ray was keeping it all up here. His mind popped open every morning like a jack-in-the-box and a new story sprang out.

'The wife in the story seems a little...'

Maggie turned towards her side, the duvet followed, like the tide creeping out.

'Yes?' Ray said.

Maggie had gone quiet.

'A little what. Tell me.'

'Superficial,' she said.

'Do you think I should change her?' Ray asked.

'No. I don't think so.'

Whenever Ray said he wanted to write something new, Maggie just shrugged and said, let's open the window. That was their joke. Open the window and chuck the money out. Ray saw his bag of dimes spinning in mid-air, dropping onto the concrete like rain.

'Are you okay?' he asked.

'Yes, just sleepy.' Her voice withdrew.

She was out like a light. Ray lay next to her, the story still hadn't finished with him, his mind kept clocking in on half hour installments. 'The Fireman'. Was it a good enough title? What tempature did paper burn at? He should write that down. Make a list of places to call to find out tomorrow. The chemistry department. Finally, a yawn overtook him.

In the middle of the night, Maggie's side of the bed was covered in wrinkles, the duvet slid from his shoulders as he sat up. The light blazed in the hallway and he heard her through the wall talking to his daughter. 'Sssshh. Ssssh.' The baby cried on.

The first thing I thought when I checked my word count on Day 30 of NaNoWriMo was SHIT. Jean Rhys may have been a reclusive alcoholic but she still had the pragmatism to appropriate a character from a novel 100 years out of copyright. I'd thought of *Wide Sargasso Sea* off and on throughout my draft of 50,000 words. Why wasn't I more like Rhys? Her prose was incandesent, her point of view beautifully sustained throughout that short brutal novel. Bronte's *Jane Eyre* was the pyre on which *Wide Sargasso Sea* burned. Even if Rhys was bat shit mental.

I put my draft into a folder on my desktop and went back to school. I took a class in creative non-fiction at Victoria University. The class was perched on top of a small gnarly hill. I passed a cemetary on the way up the hill each week and felt great empathy for the lives now shelved inside, each headstone bookended by a pair of dates: the beginning and the end. The trouble for me was always the bit in the middle.

My fellow students were not to be underestimated. After one of my metaphors was maimed by a 20-year-old, I met the course tutor, Harry Ricketts, for a coffee. Ricketts was British and polite. A prolific author and poet, he'd escaped the tyranny of the novel. He suggested I could, too.

'What do you want to write?' he asked.

'I wanted to rewrite *Fahrenhiet 451* from the perspective of the female characters but I failed.' I outlined my flop. 'My book turned into a farce.'

He contained his diplomacy. 'Then why don't you write about that?'

'Okay.' I finished my flat white and stood up.

Maybe I could put Iggle Piggle in it?

My rebooted draft was now a book about a book. But at least the book it was about was Ray Bradbury's *Fahrenhiet 451*. I had held his masterpiece up as a lens to examine my career as a chain-bookseller. Borders had been extinguished but the ashes were kind of funny.

I sent *Tinderbox* to three agents.

Number 1 didn't write back.

Number 2 told me that my lead character was shallow.

Number 3 skyped to ask how much I knew about Judy Blume? Because a book about Blume could really find a market. I confessed I'd never read anything by Blume – except the title of *Are you there God? It's me, Margaret* in passing, as I shelved it in the young adult section at Borders. (Coincidentially, Megan is actually a the Welsh version of Margaret.)

None of the agents had read *Fahrenheit 451*. They obviously hadn't had to study it in high school.

The timer went off.

Bradbury reached into his pocket. His last dime. He span it around between his fingers – *here goes nothing* – and fed it into the typewriter. His last spurt. Montag plunged into the river and fled the mechanical hound and the city. He'd killed Captain

Beatty. Hosed him down and spun him round in a coat of flames. Bradbury hadn't even know that was going to happen. The story was moving so fast. Montag was on the train tracks now. The world opened up in ways Bradbury didn't know he was going to describe. A deer in the forest. A barn. The tenderness of it all. Damn. It was good. It was a good story. Montag came upon the train tracks and met the book people. Granger stood up from the fire and welcomed Montag back from the dead.

This is my favourite scene in *Fahrenheit 451*.

SparkNotes described Granger as the leader of the 'Book People.' But I imagined his stature as that of a Borders manager who liked to lead from the back. The book people at the end of Bradbury's novel were just five out-of-work blokes, a former chair of Cambridge, a doctor, a professor of ethics, a Reverend and Granger – who is the author of a book titled *The Fingers in the Glove; The Proper Relationship between the Individual and Society.*

The men introduced themselves to Montag as the masterworks they've learnt by heart. Plato. Schopenhauer. Darwin. Einstein. Aristophanes and Gandhi. Turns out there aren't that many light reads in the woods. I can't imagine most of us will ever read Plato or the Hebrew bible first hand. Including me. So perhaps Bradbury was right? Technology has shortcircuited our knowledge and we're trapped in a culture of ever diminishing returns. Yet I like to think I stand for freedom of speech. At least I stand in line for it.

Library checkouts continue to be automated like supermarket queues in order to aid efficency. The Great Library of Alexandria is responding to changing business models;

growing in some areas, declining in others, transforming to match customer demand. Ray Bradbury wrote five short stories set in libraries before he struck *Fahrenheit 451*. He kept returning to the image of man as a book. So did I. But what if the man was a megalomaniac? The book a farce? In my mind the image of 'man as book' had fused with Jeff Bezos, for better or for worse.

SparkNotes said that Mildred was frightening because her character was completely unreadable. But I didn't believe that. In my novel Mildred wanted the story struck straight from the wick of her life, burning brightly.

Truffaut's film was critisced for neglecting the science fiction elements of Bradbury's original text. But one of Truffaut's achievements is that he showed how quickly technology can carbon-date. In a scene at the fire department Oskar Werner demonstrated to a bunch of new cadets the various hiding places for books. He flicked the switch on an electric toaster. Zap! Two paperbacks. Sometimes book people pop up where you least expect them.

For some time indie bookstores have been reappearing. The author and owner of Parnassus Bookstore, Ann Patchett, has called it a comeback. And even Jeff Bezos is on board. In 2016, Amazon opened a physical bookstore. It seems counter intuitive, even corrupt, for Amazon to cash in on the last refuge of the analogue: community. But there's good news out there too. Sales of e-books have plateaued. They are, after all, still a bit shit. And under the tuteledge of James Daunt Waterstones has evicted the Kindle Fire from its shelves. But it's not just a case of one format or the other. I bet most people now read a lot of content digitally, with all the windows on their devices open.

No-one in their right mind can pity the demise of a chain store. Not even me. Yet I've wound up in a Facebook group for ex-Borders employees. There are over 8000 members, including the former CEO of Borders UK.

Old merchanidse flows on to the page. A teddy bear tangled in a comments thread. A Borders box from Store 74 in Pittsburgh. A reciept from Store 285 in Washington DC.

What's the dumbest question a customer ever asked you?

Who wrote the diary of Anne Frank?

I want the original Bible. The one Jesus would have used.

Do you have SparkNotes for Nicholas Sparks books?

A quick check on the SparkNotes website tells me they don't. Nicholas doesn't need his sparks decoded. *The Notebook* comes with an open heart.

So do most of the members of the Facebook group. The tone is upbeat. The book people post book porn. The most beautiful libraries in the world. Cats spreadeagled over centrefolds, pages parted. Mugs bolstered by heartwarming mantras. *I am a book dragon not a book worm. A house is not a home without books. Its not hoarding if it's books.*

I confess to a certain fatigue with this smiley faced pro-book endorsement. Maybe my heart has been blackened like Captain Beatty's? Or perhaps I am just tired of preaching to the converted?

The Borders alumni die, get cancer and lose their homes. Help out an old Borders peeps! Givealittle. Learnalot. Connect, Disconnect.

The content providers, still providing content.

It was the best job I ever had. Sad face.

I sit on the borders of love. I've never posted anything but I watch.

At the end of my rewrite of F451, the book people were recruiting. The pay was shit but it was an opportunity to be part of something bigger than yourself.

And it wasn't only Montag who survived the war. I hated the suggestion latent in Bradbury's text that Mildred was asking for it, as though her vanity deserved the bombs that flattened the city at the end of the book. Don't we all deserve peace whether we're shallow or not? And isn't the extension of peace to our enemies our most luxurious and hazardous freedom? At the end of my draft Mildred and the mechanical hound were waiting to join the book people. The future might need a bookseller with a taste for the mainstream. Especially if she looks like Julie Christie. The mechanical hound, like the Ereader, had turned out to be less of a threat than first imagined. Reprogrammed, the hound could even quote Dostoevsky, thereby letting readers with a short attention span off the hook.

I let Clarisse live too. I saw by the end that Bradbury was right. Her face really was soft and gentle like a fragile milk crystal. Whatever the heck milk crystal was. And Francois Truffaut had helped me understand the importance of beauty – its terrible potential for disruption – by casting Julie Christie in the roles of both the revolutionary and the bored housewife.

At the end of my draft, the mechanical hound looked up at the moon and thought about howling. Then wondered if it was a bit OTT.

Night crouched on the the other side of the shore.

The hound comprehended that the moon was round, it rose and fell with the tides, its image waxed and waned in fiction and in fact. That same old moon had slept with writers good, bad and inbetween. The moon inside Janet's Frame's *The Lagoon* lived under water, dim and secret. Whereas the moon in *The Mighty Boosh* was just Noel Fielding covered in whipped cream. 'When you are the moon, the best form you can be is a full moon.'

The moon in all quarters has hosted astronauts and illuminated manuscripts in the deepset windows of monastries, the moon saw the arrival and displacement of the Gutenberg Press, it hung above Allen Lane's head as he slept and a train blew steam across the tracks near Agatha Christie's house. The next morning he found himself at Exeter Station Platform, hands in pockets. He looked over at a nearby vending machine. What he really wanted was something light to read. He glanced around the platform at the idle commuters. Imagine a vending machine that dispensed books! When his train finally exited the station that morning, the pale moon lagged behind, just an outline in the sky, clouds chugging.

If Jeff Bezos ever does make it into space, the moon will be there waiting. No matter what happens during the day the moon comes out every night, powered by the sun's electricity.

Incidentally, SparkNotes wasn't originally set up to support student study. It was founded by four harvard graduates as an online dating site, first called Pimpin' Cupid, later, The Spark. The Harvard graduates behind the site realised they had a captive student demographic and branched out into providing contemporary study guides.

Bradbury had at least two affairs during his marriage to Maggie. One began on his fiftieth birthday, when the phone in his office rang. Bradbury picked up and a female voice had said: 'It's your birthday, you're alone and your wife and children have forgotten.'

What a line! Forget the dandelion and go straight for the jugular.

Postscript: Bradbury didn't face any major copyright issues when he published *Fahrenheit 451*, despite his liberal use of quotations. My situation was a little different. I found a publisher prepared to take my book on. It wasn't about money. (I didn't have any.) It was about integrity. (Clunk.) I wrote to the Ray Bradbury Estate asking for permission to use his characters. I toyed with the letter. Procrastinating. I called my book a homage to *Fahrenheit 451*. I emailed the letter.

A reply arrived back poste haste. They wanted to see the book. I sent excerpts. Carefully edited excerpts that were respectful. After all I did respect Bradbury, didn't I? Another quick reply. They wanted to see the *whole* draft.

Gulp. Nothing I had read about Bradbury made me feel optimistic. Apparently Ray Bradbury thought Andy Warhol was a thief. Bradbury's imagination was big but it still had limits. I had graduated from art school, grew up admiring Warhol and I really was a thief. In the late 90s I used to rent mainstream movies from the local video store and burn them into experimential videos in the manual edit suite at art school. I gave big budget films different soundtracks. I altered the narrative arcs. I didn't think of it as stealing. I thought of it as art. However my brilliant career as a video artist quickly blew a fuse. White fuzzy lines begin to run through the video tape whenever I tried to burn copies in the edit suite. Macrovision was an early form of digital rights management that added invisible signals to commerical VHS tapes making it impossible to produce copies in a second VHS recorder. Shit.

Here I am – two decades later and still poaching from the classics.

An email arrived in my inbox. 'The Bradbury family have read and discussed your novel and they are uncomfortable with your use of the excerpts from Ray Bradbury's FAHRENHEIT 451.'

It was the word uncomfortable that got to me. I was uncomfortable that they were uncomfortable. I didn't want to write a book about someone else's book. I couldn't comfort them. I couldn't comfort myself. I couldn't pretend that my affection for Fahrenheit 451 was straightforward. Or that Ray Bradbury was entirely real to me. Let alone his family.

I could have pursued my right to his characters. But what right did I have? I had taken the master's vision and sullied it with my own silly thoughts. I am the white clown; I can't seperate my face from the mask. I hijacked Bradbury's vision of a future without books to try and say something but what? Technology and paperbacks can coexist? Clarisse isn't innocent. Mildred isn't a bitch. Return to sender. Freedom of speech seemed like a lofty conceit when pitted against intellectual copyright.

After his remake of *Fahrenheit 451* was a flop with the critics and the public, Truffaut wrote Bradbury an apology *Je suis désolé*.

It was noble of Truffaut to apologise, a mark of the auteur's character.

I owed Bradbury an apology too. I had set my book inside his, like a cuckoo laying its egg in another's nest.

I felt ridiculous. *Sooty.*

I filed the hard copy of the letter from the estate in my underwear drawer where it remains with pairs of nylon pants that no longer fit. The letter has a small window. I can peer through the pane and browse the lines of my own address. This is as close to Ray Brabury as I will ever get.

Most of the moments in my life are moments spent not writing. Bradbury didn't have this problem. When he died on June 5, 2012, at the age of 91, he had published more than five hundred works including short stories, novels, plays, screenplays and verse. Yet his tombstone simply reads: author of *Fahrenheit 451*. The novel remains his most famous work; every banned books day the internet is aflame with quotes from *Fahrenheit 451*. Bradbury's classic dystopia stands for freedom of speech and love of literature worldwide.

I recently read Bradbury's book *Zen and the Art of Writing*. If there is anyone who needs this book it's me. I am the least Zen person I know. This is Ray's mantra: Work. Relax. Don't think. I think he's right. Creativity comes from the subconscious mind. That's where Iggle Piggle came from. Iggle Piggle is beyond censorship, especially self-censorship. People often say I think I've got a book in me. Well, I thought I had a book in me too. But it turned out that I actually had Ray Bradbury's book in me.

I tried to rewrite *Fahrenheit 451*. Permission denied. Autobiography: the consolation prize. I knew I wasn't going to rise from the flames like the phoenix emblazoned on the uniform of Bradbury's firemen. But perhaps like the salamander I could scuttle out of the fire and live within it, despite it? I could evade my predators by using tail autonomy.

In the morning I got up, shelved the letter from the Estate in my underwear drawer and read Bloom's *Modern Critical Interpretation*. Bloom begins by spelling out that *Fahrenheit 451* is a period piece, noting, 'this short, thin, rather tendentious novel has an ironic ability to inhabit somewhat diverse periods'. Totes. I found the rest of the essays in the book academic and boring. Even the one titled 'To Build a Mirror Factory: The Mirror and Self-examination in Ray Bradbury's *Fahrenheit 451*'.

Bradbury was once a consultant for NASA. In 2009 he told the *New York Times* that the Internet wasn't real, it was just out there in the air somewhere. Fair point, but *Fahrenheit 451* isn't real either and now it's in the air too.

Online the fan fiction is teeming like rain. In 'Water Droplets Falling' by Ashleigh12917, Clarisse looks back over her shoulder and sees Montag taste the rain. Then she tastes the rain again, anew. Perhaps this is a metaphor for the relationship between author and reader? In her last moments Ashleigh12917's Clarisse feels only the tingly sensation of water droplets falling, unfettered by the Bradbury Estate.

Most of the *Fahrenheit 451* fan fiction runs out of steam after a few paragraphs. Like me, the fans only manage to emit sparks. Not many have taken on the narrative from Mildred's perspective, except Angelcupcake1. In her story 'My Lost Love' Mildred tears up old photographs of Montag, her cheeks as rosy as a peach. You go girl.

I closed my laptop and walked to Aro Video. Spring was on the make. The sky clear of clouds. My work safely stored in the cloud. I was free to be just another pedestrian. Aro Video is housed in a two story wooden villa on a friendly street populated by other Indies. Pedestrians sat crosslegged outside cafes: flat whites, flat screens. Outside the video shop a box of discounted stock.

At the counter the owner told me, 'You can sponsor a DVD.'

'Can I sponsor *Fahrenheit 451*?' I asked.

'No. That's not how the scheme works.' He told me about their new patronage system. Customers can contribute money towards the purchase of new titles – DVDs that are not already in the store catalogue. It's part of their effort to stay afloat in the wake of online streaming and illegal downloads.

'But I want to sponsor *Fahrenheit 451*,' I said. 'Maybe you should invent a new scheme where people can pay to sponsor their favourite DVD.'

The owner frowned. I outlined the concept again but he wasn't buying.

I paid my late fines and rented Truffaut's *Fahrenheit 451* for the upteeneth time. I could have watched it on YouTube but it's not the same. YouTube doesn't have the DVD extras. It's what happened behind the scenes that really interested me. How else could I have learnt about the film's editor Thom Noble, who would go on to win an Oscar for his work on *Thelma and Louise*? Or Ann Bell the young actress whose best scene was lost on the cutting room floor? Bell would later star in *Tenko* (*Tenko!* I fucking loved *Tenko*, especially the opening title sequence of that red moon prisoned behind barbed wire). Or that the composer Bernard Hermann had worked exclusively with string and perscussion instruments on the soundtrack – including the jaunty xylophone that accompanied the bright red fire engine as it raced round the set of Pinewood studios, burning rubber.

'So why this again? Are you studying the film?' the video store owner asked.

'No. I'm writing a book about *Fahrenheit 451*.' I explained the ruckus with the estate. The end of Borders.

The knowledgable owner looked uncomfortable.

'Sounds a bit meta,' he said.

'Yes, it is a bit meta,' I reached up and touched my face, cheek burning. Time for another apology. 'That's the last thing we need,' I said.

What do they look like: the booksellers of the future? What do they think about in cities we can only imagine through the lens of science fiction? Do paperbacks still exist? Do people continue to type? Has the Kindle been eradicated, its memory wiped? Imagine a world with no internet. A lonely search engine evacuated; the sun seen through a gauze of smog; the moon its pale fascimile. But maybe the future has turned out simpler than we ever dreamed.

The white page. The cave wall. The wavering screen. A finger swiped across a tablet, a quill dipped in ink, the nib of a pen quivering, sniffing out the scent of a new story.

Now.

Are you ready for the SparkNotes *Fahrenheit 451* quiz?

It took me fifteen seconds to answer the quiz. I only got one question wrong.

Q. Which of the following is not presented as a reason why books are banned in the future?

    1. Other forms of entertainment become more popular.
    2. Books contain ideas that might undermine authority.
    3. The amount of printed material is too overwhelming.
    4. Books make people feel inferior.

The timer went off.

Incendiary Notes

This is a work of non-fiction. Names, characters, businesses, places, events and incidents are, sadly, not the products of my imagination. Including Nicky Boardman the general manager I worked for at Borders Norwich. In 2015 Nicky died – at 34-years-old – from a rare type of cancer. Nicky was one in a million. After Borders UK was liquidated he wrote over 500 references for ex-employees. I hope he's been promoted to God.

Also, I think I should state for the record that a group of staff at Borders Norwich once complained that I was a nightmare to work with. My crimes included shouting and refusing to give a staff member a toilet break. I have nothing to offer in my defence.

I did finish NaNoWriMo in 2013. I wrote 50,000 words. Most were incoherent. It's taken a few more matches to strike *Tinderbox*. The draft I finally sent out to agents pitted my failed rewrite of the novel against my failed Borders career. Truffaut's film entered the frame late in the piece because I needed a way to write about *Fahrenheit 451* without writing directly about Bradbury's characters. And I felt sorry for Truffaut. His film was a flop too.

Recently I was amused to come across film critic Pauline Kael's original review of *Fahrenheit 451*. For Kael the whole conceit was a bad idea from the get go. She said Truffaut's F451 wasn't a very good movie – but she thought the idea behind it was so naff it was actually brilliant – 'people want to see it and then want to talk about how it should have been worked out.'

I laughed. How true. Kael argues that *Fahrenheit 451* is a gimmick that turns books into totems, tapping into a kind of liberal hysteria. She points out that print is ultimately as neutral as the screen. I felt liberally hysterical reading her review. At one level I was off the hook. It's not me, it's Bradbury. But it was me too. Because I was another book fetishist that had been inflamed by his vision.

One good thing to come out of all this is that Aro Video took me up on my marketing idea and it has been a raging success. Customers love adopting their favourite film titles and they get a certificate to prove it.

Last but not least:

Dear Ray Bradbury, I never wanted to write a book about your book or a book about the film of your book but redundancy can do funny things to do a girl. It can make her uncomfortable.

Acknowledgements

Thanks to my long suffering family for their support and cheer: Rico, Fearnebot, Mum, Dad. Thanks to Jenny Downham for calm under fire, Yvonne for help with Photoshop and Kushana, the pigeon-fancier. Special thanks to all the staff at Borders who put up with me over the years and to the 2013 class of CREW 257, especially Helen Curran. And my gratitude to Harry Ricketts for first suggesting this book could be so. Last but not least thanks to Elly and Sam at Galley Beggar (I think it helped that you had both read *Fahrenhiet 451*) and to Creative New Zealand for the arts grant that enabled me to finish this book; and to my agent Veronique Baxter.

And dear Ray Bradbury: Here's to your book. I hope the future within it never ever comes true.

GALLEY BEGGAR PRESS

We hope that you've enjoyed *Tinderbox*. If you'd like to find out more about Megan, along with some of her fellow authors, head to www.galleybeggar.co.uk.

There, you will also find information about our subscription scheme, 'Galley Buddies', which is there to ensure we can continue to put out ambitious and unusual books like *Tinderbox*.

Subscribers to Galley Beggar Press:

- Receive limited black-cover editions (printed in a run of 500) of each of our four next titles.
- Have their names included in a special acknowledgments section at the back of our books.
- Are sent regular invitations to our launches, talks, and annual summer and GBP Short Story Prize parties.
- Enjoy a 20% discount code for the purchase of any of our backlist.

WHY BE A GALLEY BUDDY?

At Galley Beggar Press we don't want to compromise on the excellence of the writing we put out, or the physical quality of our books. We've been lucky enough to have had quite a few successes and prize nominations since we set up, in 2012. Over three-quarters of our authors have gone on to be longlisted, shortlisted, or the winners of over 20 of the world's most prestigious awards.

But publishing for the sake of art and for love is a risky commercial strategy. In order to keep putting out the very best books that we can, and to continue to support new and talented writers, we ourselves need some help. The money we receive from our Galley Buddy subscription scheme is an essential part of keeping us going.

By becoming a Galley Buddy, you help us to launch and foster a new generation of writers.

To join today, head to:
https://www.galleybeggar.co.uk/subscribe

FRIENDS OF GALLEY BEGGAR PRESS

Galley Beggar Press would like to thank the following individuals, without the generous support of whom our books would not be possible:

Stuart Armstrong • Martin Bainbridge • Edward Baines • Jaimie Batchan • Rachel Barnes • Alison Bianchi • Mark Blackburn • Edwina Bowen • John Brooke • Max Cairnduff • Stuart Carter • Leigh Chambers • Paul Crick • Alan Crilly • Jonathan Dawid • Paul Dettman • Janet Dowling • Gerry Feehily • Lydia Fellgett • Robert Foord • Simon Fraser • Paul Fulcher • Elaine Glaser • Neil Griffiths • Robbie Guillory • George Hawthorne • David Hebblethwaite • Penelope Hewett Brown • Ann Hirst • Sandra Horn • Sylvia Horner • Bex Hughes • Ruth Hunt • Heidi James • Alice Jolly • Diana Jordison • Riona Judge McCormack • Lesley Kissin • Wendy Laister • Sue and Tony Leifer • Philip Lane • Jackie Law • Philip Makatrewicz • Anil Malhotra • Tom Mandall • Cerith Mathias • Adrian Masters • Jon McGregor • Malachi McIntosh • Leona Medlin • Marilyn Messenger • Tina Meyer • James Miller • Linda Nathan • Dean Nicholls • Catherine Nicholson • Seb Ohsan-Berthelsen • Liz O'Sullivan • Eliza O'Toole • Victoria Parsons • Radhika Pandit • Roland Pascoe • Alex Preston • Richard Price • Polly Randall • Bronwen Rashad • Barbara Renel • Pete Renton • Ian Rimell • Jack Roberts • David Rose • Libby Ruffle • Ellie Rycroft • Richard Sheehan • Matthew Shenton • Chris Smith • Michael Spoor • Nicholas Stone • Ashley Tame • Preti Taneja • Ewan Tant • Justine Taylor • Sam Thorp • James Torrance • Eloise Touni • Anthony Trevelyan • Kate Triggs • Anna Vaught • Stephen Walker • Steve Walsh • Rosita Wilkins • Eley Williams • Bianca Winter • Emma Woolerton • Ben Yarde-Buller • Ian Young • Sara Zo • Rupert Ziziros • Carsten Zwaaneveld

Tinderbox